ember

a journal of luminous things

D1133909

edited by Brian James Lewis

Ember: A Journal of Luminous Things
Volume 1, Issue 2

10 9 8 7 6 5 4 3 2 1

ISBN: 978-1-68073-041-8 (Trade Paperback)

Cover art: *Frog and Sister Moon* by Keliana Tayler.
Copyright © 2014 Keliana Tayler. Licensed and used by permission.

Interior illustrations by Casey Robin.
Copyright © 2015 Casey Robin. Licensed and used by permission.
Learn more at *caseyrobin.com.*

Ember: A Journal of Luminous Things is administered and published by the Empire & Great Jones Creative Arts Foundation, a registered 501(c)(3) non-profit corporation. Learn more at *EmberJournal.org.*

The RawengulkSans font used in headings and the ember logo was developed by **gluk**. It can be found along with many other typefaces as *glukfonts.pl.*

Page numbers are presented in Corbel, a Microsoft ClearType font. All other text is Minion Pro, an Adobe Originals typeface.

Empire & Great Jones Creative Arts Foundation
Brian Lewis, President
6100 Horseshoe Bar Road, Suite A-133
Loomis, CA 95650
USA

IF YOU RECEIVED A COPY of this journal for free, in print or electronic format, please consider making a donation in support of great writing (and the authors in this collection) at *EmberJournal.org/support.*

About the Cover Artist

"Frog and Sister Moon" by artist **Keliana Tayler** was specially commissioned to go with the short story "The Frog Who Swallowed the Moon" which appears in this second issue of *Ember*.

Limited Edition prints, hand-embellished by the artist, are available for purchase at *store.egjpress.org/art/sister-moon*.

Keliana was born in Provo, Utah. When she was about five years old, her father started work on an online comic and so, to spend time with him, she began to draw. By the time she entered high school, she knew that she wanted to pursue an artistic career.

Keliana is currently chasing down that dream at full speed. She attends college at Southern Utah University, aiming to graduate in 2017 as a Bachelor of Fine Arts with an emphasis in illustration. She pays for this education with her art, and her commissioned work for small companies and individual buyers has appeared in many venues. Despite standing with one foot in a professional boot and the other in a student's, she presses herself for excellence in all endeavors.

Keliana's mediums range from traditional to modern, and she works just as comfortably in watercolor and colored pencil as digital painting and drawing. She places particular emphasis character design and story illustration.

"Art is always better when there's a story behind every piece," she says. "Seeing people connect with the story, be it hidden in the paint or written in the artist's statement, is why I love doing what I do."

Find more of Keliana Tayler's work or contact her regarding a custom commission at *kiki-tayler.deviantart.com*.

Prints of "Frog and Sister Moon" are available through the E&GJ Little Press store at *store.egjpress.org/art/ember* and are suitable for framing.

About the Illustrator

Casey Robin is an illustrator and visual development artist working out of Southern California. Her clients include Walt Disney Animation Studios, Random House, and Zondervan Publishing. She has studied art and animation at CSSSA, CalArts, Studio Art Centers International, The Illustration Academy at Ringling, and more. Her fine art is represented by ArtInsights Animation and Film Art Gallery.

Casey Robin has made pictures for print, film, and the web. Her favorite things to draw are fairy tale characters and adorable girls. She has a strong taste for whimsy and cuteness, but is equally intrigued by melancholy and monsters. Currently, she is hard at work developing her first solo book, taking occasional breaks to converse with her fat cat, Oliver.

Find a selected portfolio at *caseyrobin.com* or purchase prints of her fine art in her shop at *etsy.com/shop/CaseyRobinArt.*

Each illustration in *Ember* was created after Casey personally read and enjoyed the piece it accompanies. Individual prints of the artwork—or the entire collection of twenty-one pieces—can be purchased through the E&GJ Little Press store at *store.egjpress.org/art/ember.*

All prints are suitable for framing.

Contents
Volume 1, Issue 2

for younger readers

 Featured Young Authors

for older readers

for younger readers

The stories in this section may be most appropriate for middle-grade readers—but can be enjoyed by everyone.

The Frog Who Swallowed the Moon
by Renee Carter Hall

I N THE EARLIEST DAYS, Frog had a beautiful voice. All through the long summer twilights, he sang sweetly among the reeds while fireflies blinked lazily and the earth settled itself into evening. Around that first pond, the other creatures always gathered to listen.

"Such a lovely voice," Salamander said.

"Just marvelous," Turtle added.

"So sweet and clear," Mallard said with a sigh. "How *do* you do it?"

Frog always looked embarrassed and gave the only answer he could think of, which was also the truth. "I don't know. I just love singing."

One night, having sung a particularly long tune about how beautiful the moon was and how sweet the summer breeze and how wonderful it was simply to be alive, Frog drew a bucket of water from the pond to soothe his dry throat. The full moon shone like a silver coin on the surface of the water, and Frog gulped the

---

ABOUT THE AUTHOR

Renee Carter Hall works as a medical transcriptionist by day and as a writer, poet, and artist all the time. Her short fiction has appeared in a variety of publications, including Strange Horizons, Black Static, Daily Science Fiction, and the Anthro Dreams podcast. She lives in West Virginia with her husband, their cat, and a ridiculous number of creative works-in-progress.

— *www.reneecarterhall.com*
Twitter: @RCarterHall

whole bucketful down.

The night went black around him, like a candle blown out.

Frog swallowed hard, hiccuped, burped, and swallowed again. It felt like a stone had settled in his belly. "Oh, dear," he said—and every time he opened his mouth, moonlight burst out. "Oh, *dear.*"

Everyone had gone home after Frog's last song, and being all alone made things even scarier. Keeping his mouth slightly open so he could see the way, Frog hopped to Salamander's home among the damp stones and dead leaves at the edge of the pond.

Salamander listened to Frog's story, shielding his eyes with one hand against the flashes of light that came with every word.

"What does it feel like?" Salamander asked.

"Sort of cold and fizzy," Frog said miserably. "What should I do?"

"We'll go see Turtle. He's older than any of us. He'll know what to do."

When they reached Turtle's mossy log, they had to knock on his shell several times before he emerged, blinking sleepily, to ask what was the matter.

"Frog's swallowed the moon," Salamander said.

"Dreams and nonsense. Go back to sleep."

"But it's true." Salamander nudged Frog, and Frog opened his mouth. Blue-white light flooded the log.

Turtle squinted at them. "Hm. Thought it was a little darker than usual tonight. What'd you ever do such a silly thing for, anyway?"

"I didn't mean to. It just happened."

Turtle sighed a deep, slow, heavy sigh, as if this sort of thing had happened a dozen times before and he was heartily sick of dealing with it. "Well, there's only one creature in this pond who can help you, and it isn't me. You'll have to go see the Sister of the Moon."

"Who's she?" Salamander asked.

"She lives in the center-of-the-center of the pond. You'll have to take the moonpath to get there."

"But there's no—" Frog's moonlight blinded them all again when he spoke, so he tried to move his mouth as little as possible. "There's no path out there. I've been all over the pond since I was a tadpole. And the only thing in the center is some mud and marsh-reeds."

"Didn't take the moonpath, though, did you?"

"No, but—"

"Then it wasn't the center-of-the-center, was it?"

Frog looked at Salamander. Salamander shrugged.

"I guess not," Frog said.

"Of course it wasn't. Only full moonlight shows the path, and then you have to be looking for it. So go on with you, and look." With that, Turtle pulled back into his shell, muttering about lost sleep and unexpected company and how you could certainly bring a bit of fish or at least a nice worm or two if you were going to wake someone up in the middle of the night for such a silly problem as swallowing the moon.

Salamander followed Frog back to the edge of the pond. The water lay dark and still, and stars shone on the surface like white speckles on a black egg. Frog opened his mouth, and the beam of moonlight speared the blackness, skipping over the surface of the water. Then a soft glow appeared, and another, and another, each following the last, until a path of pale stones shone in the moonlight, leading out into the water.

"The moonpath," Frog whispered.

"Do you want me to go with you?" Salamander was whispering, too, and he sounded like he hoped the answer was no.

Frog swallowed. The moon in his belly felt colder and heavier. "I guess I'd better go alone."

From the edge of the pond, the stones looked hardly large enough to hop onto, but they were dry and just rough enough to keep Frog's webbed feet from slipping. He glanced back at Salamander, who waved and tried to smile. Frog was about to smile back when he saw that the stones behind him had already disappeared. He swallowed again, faced forward, and went on.

It didn't seem to be the pond he'd known as a tadpole. In the stark light of his moonbeam, the pale stones led him across an expanse of water larger than he'd ever seen before. Soon there were no more marsh-reeds or cattails at the edges of his sight. There was only darkness and the moonpath, and when Frog dared to look up, even the stars had disappeared. He didn't look up again after that, keeping his light and his eyes focused on the stones just ahead.

In time, although Frog could not have said how long, there was a glimmer of silver light ahead. At first he wasn't sure if his eyes were playing tricks on him, but as he got closer to it, the light became a shape, then a structure, and at last he saw a little temple of pale stone, barely more than a roof over thin columns. The stone was veined with silver, and this was the light he'd seen. It glowed brighter as he approached.

The temple lay on a small island, just big enough to give Frog something to scramble onto as the last stone sank from underneath his feet. He rested beneath the roof, watching the veins pulse and glow like ripples on water. He had no reason to, but he felt safe.

There was no sign of anyone else, though. Where was the Sister of the Moon? And more importantly, *what* was she? He had no idea what sort of creature to look for. Whatever she was, he hoped she didn't eat frogs. He hummed a little to himself as he waited, bits of the song he'd last sung. The silver light pulsed in time with the rhythm, and he cocked his head and watched it. Light moved along the veins, drawing his gaze toward the center of the roof, where a silver bell hung. The light played over its surface until the bell seemed made of white light instead of metal.

Frog reached up and tapped it.

A clear, brilliant note sounded. It became part of the stone, part of the light, part of Frog himself. Its perfect tone ached within him, and he knew that anything beautiful he heard from now on would be compared to it.

Beyond the temple, the dark water stirred. A white shape moved beneath it, turning in slow arcs. It rose closer to the surface, and finally Frog saw a white fish, bigger than any he'd ever seen, far bigger than he was, with scales that glittered white and silver. Her fins trailed out behind, translucent and delicate as frost. Silent as fog on the water she came closer, until Frog could see every scale, every ridge of her fins, and the flat, sharp disc of her eye.

"Sister of the Moon," Frog whispered.

So I have been. So I am. So I shall be.

Her voice sent ripples through his mind. It didn't hurt, but it felt strange, almost ticklish. *You carry my sister.*

"It was an accident."

It must have taken great power to pull her from the sky.

"Not really," Frog mumbled. "I just sort of swallowed it. Her. By accident," he repeated, wanting to make that part of it clear, at

least.

Ah. Her fins rippled as she turned slowly in the water, eying him. *Moon and water are tricksters. So they have been, so they shall be. Better than you, master Frog, have been snared.*

He felt a little better after that. She was odd, but at least she didn't seem angry with him. In fact, she almost seemed a little amused, though it was hard to read a fish's expression. So he told her what had happened, and then she *did* laugh, in a mist of bubbles.

I could have chosen a far worse guardian for my sister's light. Will you carry her always, so that I call you brother, or shall we return her to the sky?

"I'd much rather put her back, ma'am. Er—your majesty?"

She waved his concern away with a slow fan of her tail. *There is a price, of course.*

Frog nodded. He'd heard enough strange old tales to know that much.

Pondflesh can only bear so much of my sister's power. I can call her from your body, but your voice, I am afraid, will not be as it was.

Frog stared at her. "Will I still be able to sing?"

After a fashion, yes. But your voice will be a rough echo of what it is now. You have had the sweet; this will be bitter. You have had the light; this will be shadow.

Frog thought of the warm summer nights, his friends gathered around to listen. He thought of the joy of hitting each note, of adding something beautiful to the stillness around him, until his voice seemed like an extension of the night itself. Then he looked up into the dark sky, and thought of it staying dark.

"It really isn't much of a choice, is it," he said quietly.

There are always choices. There are not always pleasant ones.

The sympathy in her voice gave him courage. "All right." He stood up as straight as a frog could. "What do I do?"

Only sing, and that will be my gift to you.

He remembered the song he'd sung earlier that evening—if it was still the same night, which he was no longer sure of. A song about the beauty of the moon, and the wonder of being alive. The opening notes floated into his memory, and he sang.

It was the same song, but bigger, richer, sweeter. It was the moon and everything it looked upon. There was the same joy, the same beauty, but there was an edge of sorrow, a rim of shadow like the moon held just as it began to wane from full. It was his same voice, but the way he might have sounded after singing all his life, deeper, purer. There was no effort, no thought, only song pouring out in utter perfection. Somewhere he began to weep, and yet he sang on, in a song that became all his longings and strivings and dreams given voice. And then he felt it ebb, felt the light slipping away from him, drawn out of his body. Part of him wanted to clutch at it, pull it back. The rest of him merely watched it go.

The last note died away. Frog took a ragged breath and looked up. The sky was scattered with stars, and among them the moon hung full. He swallowed. The heaviness was gone, and his throat was sore. He felt cold, and empty, and tired.

The first word he tried to say came out so rough it was barely a sound.

Gently.

"I'll … never sing again, will I? Not like before."

No.

Sudden anger closed his throat. "Why did you call that a gift? Why give me that, to remember, when I can never—"

Her sadness washed over him. *What is the memory of joy but a gift?*

Frog gave a shuddering sigh and blinked away hot tears. "Well. At least it's all right again." He looked up at the moon again, trying to feel satisfied, trying to feel pleased. "I guess I'd better get home, before they start worrying."

The Sister of the Moon stirred her fins. *Farewell, then, brother Frog. May you find a voice again, and remember joy.* Then she dropped deeper into the water, her faint light moving away, and in the ripples of her wake, the stones rose up one by one to lead him home.

No one saw Frog around the pond the next day. Salamander took him licorice tea with honey for his throat. Frog said he was fine, though he knew he didn't sound fine, but he didn't tell Salamander what had happened, and Salamander didn't ask. That was why they were friends, and Frog was grateful. Besides, everyone had seen the moon come back to the sky, and that was all that mattered—or so Frog told himself.

As evening came on, Frog huddled in the corner of his reed house. If this were any other night, he thought, he would have been out by the water, greeting his friends, thinking of what songs he might sing. Instead, he felt like going as far away as he could from the pond and never coming back.

He wondered if they were still out there, Turtle and Mallard and Salamander and all the others, waiting for him.

Reeds rustled. "It's me," Salamander said. "How's your throat?"

"Better."

They sat in silence for a moment.

"Are they out there?" Frog asked finally.

"They'd like to see you. They've been worried."

"I don't know."

Salamander nodded. "I'll tell them you're all right."

"Maybe tomorrow night," Frog said.

Salamander nodded again. "Because—I mean—you're more than just your voice, you know." He hesitated, then slipped through the reeds.

Late that night, when everyone else was asleep, Frog sat by the black water, gazing at the moon.

After a fashion, he thought, remembering the Sister's words.

No one would hear.

He had to try sometime.

He drew a breath and opened his mouth. It sounded more like a belch than a note.

He went home.

"Why bother?" he told Salamander several nights later. "It's not even singing, really, anymore."

"But you love it."

Frog sipped his licorice tea. "I used to. Not now."

It was a lie, of course, and they both knew it, but neither pointed it out. That was why they were friends.

Frog told the others it hurt too much to sing now. That wasn't a lie, though it was a pain that no amount of licorice or honey could ever ease.

And yet, he *did* miss it. Not just the summer twilights and the expectant hush of the audience and the praise that came after. He missed the feeling of it, the way a song rose in him and demanded to be sung. But every time he tried, all he could remember was the brilliance of that moon-song, the Sister's cursed gift, that perfection he could never even strive for anymore. And so night passed into night, and except for the crickets, the nights were silent.

"If I could forget how it was before," Frog told Salamander, "maybe I could be happy."

Salamander sipped his tea. "Maybe you could forget just for a little while. You know. *Pretend* to forget."

"Mm," Frog said.

In the end, it was the full moon, again, that was Frog's undoing. One warm, clear, windless night, the beauty of it all tugged at him, and a new song welled up, and without thinking he gave it voice. The sound still disappointed him, but he was getting used to it, and this time he tried singing higher and lower, drawing the notes out, then clipping them short. It wasn't anything like the voice he'd had before—and it still hurt that it never would be—but maybe …

So he pretended to forget, for a little while. He set aside the perfect beauty of a silver bell and a white moon and listened instead to the mud and the reeds of Frog, to what it was and to what it might be.

The sound of his new voice didn't surprise him anymore. But the happiness—the crazy, rough-edged, imperfect happiness—did.

He thought of new songs and practiced them far from the pond, where no one else could hear. At last, when he felt at least half ready, he told Salamander, and Salamander told the others, and once again the creatures of the pond gathered to listen. He sang quick and low, earthy and bold, a song about the strangeness of the moonpath and a sky dark of stars. It was rough, but there was life in it. There was joy in it.

When the last note died away, heart pounding, he waited.

The silence hung like cold fog. He watched one look to the other. No one seemed to know what to say.

"That's very … innovative," Turtle managed. "Quite clever of you."

"I've never heard anything like it," Mallard said brightly.

One by one they drifted away, their polite comments hitting him like raindrops. Some rolled off. Some soaked in. Salamander was the last to remain.

"Give them time," he said softly. "They'll learn to love it."

Frog swallowed. "Maybe sometimes I am just a voice."

"Maybe," Salamander said. "But not to everyone."

And that was why they were friends.

In these later days, Frog has a beautiful voice. No crowds gather at that first pond now, to praise his songs' sweetness and clamor for more. But there are some who still count his voice as rare and precious as before—perhaps even more so—and so he sings for them. He sings for the beauty of the world and the joy of being alive. He sings for himself, for the memories of joy and for the joy that dwells in the singing of a single, present note. And over it all the moon hangs bright and full, its light gleaming on the mirrored pond like the sound of a silver bell, its echoes rippling on and on, into the summer night.

Do Not Blow Raspberries at Monsters
by Atar Hadari

D O NOT BLOW raspberries at monsters.
Do not blow raspberries at the police.
Do not blow raspberries at little old ladies
With hair nets the colour of fleece.

Do not blow raspberries at tigers,
Nor at lions gnawing on bones.
But most of all, do not blow raspberries
at little girls carrying stones.

About the Poet

Atar Hadari's *Songs from Bialik: Selected Poems of H. N. Bialik* (Syracuse University Press) was a finalist for the American Literary Translators' Association Award and his debut poetry collection, *Rembrandt's Bible*, was published by Indigo Dreams. *Lives of the Dead: Poems of Hanoch Levin* is forthcoming from Arc Publications.

Abena and the Bride-Mad Sorcerer
by Emily Cataneo

ONCE THERE WAS a girl named Abena who lived in a town nestled in the crook between two mountains, in a stone house at the edge of a cobblestone courtyard. Abena had two younger twin sisters: one named Ndidi, who loved beautiful and glamorous curios like gilded mirrors from Berlin, and the other named Kayin, who loved to read books and spin imaginary worlds. Their mother was a seamstress who had once fallen in love with their father, a French African soldier who was stationed in their town a long time ago after a war—and who had given the girls their names.

During summer vacations, Abena loved to shelter in their dusty basement disassembling radios and telephones or inventing gadgets. Kayin and Ndidi would badger her to come play, but she would always tell them to leave her alone.

On one such day, Kayin and Ndidi banged on the basement door, shouting for Abena to come canoe with them. But Abena

---

ABOUT THE AUTHOR

Emily B. Cataneo is an American writer and freelance journalist living in Berlin, Germany. Her work has appeared in or is forthcoming from *Black Static*, *Interfictions Online: A Journal of Interstitial Arts*, and *The Dark*. When she's not writing, she can be found reading about late 19th and early 20th century history, embarking on an elaborate craft project, biking around Berlin or wearing a vintage hat.

—*emilycataneo.com*

said she was busy building a pair of wooden wings, and so Kayin and Ndidi floated alone down the river that cut through the foothills.

"I wish Abena weren't always so occupied with her stupid projects," Ndidi said.

"Should we really row so close to the far bank?" Kayin squinted at a white castle looming on the mountainside above them.

Ndidi and Kayin both knew the white castle belonged to a sorcerer, and like every child in the village, they knew that the sorcerer couldn't touch running water. They also knew they shouldn't let their boat bump against the sparkling river's opposite bank and that they certainly shouldn't climb the steep path into the shuddering dark forest.

Except that day, Ndidi, bubbling with anger at Abena, jabbed her paddle into the river and steered them towards the opposite bank. "I'll climb to the sorcerer's castle and when Abena hears what adventures I've had, she'll have to come out tomorrow." She ignored Kayin's pleas to return, and leapt onto the bank.

She climbed through the forest for about five minutes. Then something whispered on the path before her, and a figure resolved out of shadows. He was pale as the flowers that grew in the bright sunlight on the other side of the river, with moss-colored hair and sunken eyes and a long robe of filigree silver.

"A pretty girl, walking in my forest," the sorcerer said, for that was undoubtedly who he was. "Would you care to visit my castle? I can offer you many fine objects and works of art, and protect you from the dangers of the world."

Recklessness ballooned inside Ndidi as she imagined the story she might have to tell Abena. She followed the sorcerer up the winding path, wind buffeting her cheeks, until they emerged in an overgrown castle courtyard. The sorcerer led her across his threshold into a bone-white entrance hall. Glass mannequin heads wearing crowns of barbed wire stared down at her from pedestals lining the dim hall and she shuddered.

She and the sorcerer climbed a stone staircase that wound up and up and up, and with each footfall she told herself *I should turn back, the adventure has gone far enough*, but with each footfall she also told herself *just one step more, to see what will happen*.

They emerged into a windowless tower room with two doors: the one they had entered through and one at the back of the room. In the room's center loomed a tall basket woven of thin birch branches. Ndidi peered into the basket, her breath catching at the sight of the jewels and furs piled inside.

"I've grown lonely here, after all these centuries," the sorcerer said. "I'm hoping to find the right bride."

"That's ridiculous. I'm only twelve years old."

"You'll be very happy and safe here, with all the pretty things you wish your mama could afford to give you."

"No. No, I want to go home."

The sorcerer produced a jewel-studded egg from beneath his robe. "If you are to become my bride, you must not drop this egg, and you must not enter that chamber." He nodded towards a closed door at the opposite end of the room. "If you pass these tests, you will remain here as my bride, and I will kiss you half a hundred times and we will be happy forever."

Before Ndidi could protest, the sorcerer left the room and locked the door.

Ndidi charged towards the other door and threw it open. She stumbled down three steps into a shadowy room, looking left and right for a staircase down. Her hip bumped into a stone basin in the center of the room. She peered in: dark liquid, smelling of copper, sluiced inside.

She stumbled and dropped the egg into the basin, as footsteps padded on the floor behind her. She whipped around.

"I told you not to enter this room. I told you not to drop the egg," the sorcerer whispered.

His eyes did not change as he drew a knife across her throat.

Kayin paced the riverbank as the afternoon grew golden, glancing at the dark forest on the mountainside above her.

"What are you doing over there?" someone shouted.

Hans, one of the boys from the village, stood on the opposite bank, staring across the river at Kayin. Lately, Hans had acted cold towards her, and she'd heard him whispering with some of their classmates about how she and her sisters looked different from everyone else in the village. But still, she shouted back, "If I haven't returned by nightfall, tell Mama and Abena that I went to rescue Ndidi from the sorcerer."

Kayin plunged into the woods before she could change her mind. So she wouldn't be scared, she imagined she was a knight riding off to battle some great beast. As the river's burbling receded behind her, a figure materialized out of the shadows, with moss-colored hair and a long robe of shimmering greenish scales like a dragon's skin.

He was pale as the flowers, with moss-colored hair and a long robe of filigree silver.

"An imaginative girl, walking in my forest," he said. "Would you care to visit my castle? I can offer you many leather-bound books, and protect you from the dangers of the world."

Her hands shaking, Kayin followed the sorcerer up the path until they emerged at the castle. Kayin followed the sorcerer through the entrance hall, past the glass mannequin heads, and up the stone steps to the tower. With each step she thought *I should turn back,* but with each step she also thought, *I'll find Ndidi, just around this corner, and then we'll go home.*

At last they reached the top of the tower, where books overflowed the white birch basket. As Kayin bent to examine them, the sorcerer tapped her on the shoulder.

"I've grown lonely here, after all these centuries," he said. "I'm hoping to find the right bride."

"No," Kayin said, "I'm not ... I'm here to find my sister Ndidi."

The sorcerer's mouth twisted. "You'll be very happy and safe here, protected from those villagers who've started to look at you askance."

"But no, I don't want to. I want Ndidi and I—"

The sorcerer produced a glistening, scaly egg from his robes and extended it to her. "If you are to become my bride, you must not drop this egg, and you must not enter that chamber. If you pass these tests, you will remain here as my bride, and I will kiss you half a hundred times and we will be happy forever."

The sorcerer swept out of the room and closed and locked the door.

The egg quivered in Kayin's hand. She couldn't stop looking at the door across the tower. She knew she should try that door, but she also didn't want to see what lay on the other side.

But she needed to rescue Ndidi, so she crossed the tower and slid the door open.

A metallic smell assailed her. She walked forward and her shoe caught on something sticky. She stumbled into the stone pedestal in the center of the room and the egg dropped into the dark liquid sluicing inside.

A whispering of robes behind her, and the sorcerer's eyes did not change as his knife slid against her throat.

Back at the village, the streetlamps had come on. Hans—who didn't want the sorcerer to hurt Kayin and Ndidi, even though he had lately heard his parents whispering that there might be trouble for the girls soon, given all the changes in Berlin—had raised the alarm. Abena, tinkering with wooden wings in the basement, heard these shouts and raced upstairs, past Mama sobbing, into the street. Townsfolk huddled and muttered about charging up the mountainside to the sorcerer, defeating him once and for all.

Abena's cheeks grew hot when she realized she had neglected her sisters in favor of her inventions. She raced back into the house, found a flashlight and then hurried through the streets towards the river. After she rowed across, she shone her torch at the trees, illuminating hard leaves and hulking undergrowth.

A figure materialized from the forest.

"A clever girl, walking in the forest," the sorcerer said. He wore a long robe woven of wires and gears. "Would you care to visit my castle? I can offer you all the radios and telephones you could ever want, and protect you from the dangers of the world."

"I would love to come with you. Show me the way." Abena followed him through the whispering dark to his castle. As they climbed up and up the stone steps to the highest tower, she thought *I won't turn back, I'll never turn back. He won't get away with taking my sisters.*

When they entered the tower room, the sorcerer turned to her. "I've grown lonely here, after all these centuries," he said. "I'm hoping to find the right bride."

Abena lifted her chin. "I'll consider becoming your bride."

"I know who you are, you know," the sorcerer said.

"Sorry?"

"I know you are sister to the last two girls who came here. You look like them, but like no one else in your town."

"And so?"

"I suppose you truly are the cleverest, if you want to stay here as my bride. Worse fates await you at the foot of the mountain."

The hair on the back of Abena's neck crawled. *He's just trying to scare me.*

The sorcerer produced an egg, nestled on a bed of wires. "If you are to become my bride, you must not drop this egg, and you must not enter that chamber." He nodded at the door on the other side of the tower. "If you pass these tests, you will remain here as my bride, and I will kiss you half a hundred times and we will be happy forever." He swept from the room.

Abena set the egg down. Then she ran to the other door and opened it.

She clapped her hands over her nose and mouth, and recoiled

when she saw her sisters on the floor. But Abena had been studying anatomy for years, and so she bent to their bodies, and sewed them right back together, and hushed them when their eyes fluttered open and their lips parted with questions. She led them out of the secret chamber and told them to hide in the birch-bark basket, which overflowed with gleaming typewriters and delicate clocks. She scooped up the egg just as the sorcerer returned to the room.

He smiled. "You didn't drop the egg."

"I told you, I want to be your bride," she said. The sorcerer's pale lips parted, but she held up her hand. "Wait. I want to marry in the village, with Mama, and I want you to bring that—" she pointed at the basket "—as dowry."

The sorcerer nodded thoughtfully. "Very well. I accept."

"And I," Abena said, "will return to the village and prepare the wedding feast."

Abena darted into the cool night. She hurried down the mountainside, her heart racing. She arrived in the square, where all the townsfolk had gathered.

"He's coming to the village," she shouted. "How can we stop him?"

The townsfolk shouted out suggestions and advice, but the oldest woman in the village, Frau Gellern, stepped forward. "Remember why he cannot visit the village," she croaked. "He cannot touch the river. Its running water will destroy him. He fears crossing it in a boat."

Abena nodded. "In that case, I've got a plan."

Mama brought armloads of feathers from her sewing, a jar of honey, and Abena's wooden wings. She coated Abena's arms with the honey, spread the feathers over them and strapped the wings to Abena's back. She also brought a mask, wooden with bright painted designs, that Abena's father had given to her before he returned to Africa, a long time ago. Then Abena, wearing her father's mask and her own invention, led the way back to the river, where she spread her wings and soared across, trembling with nervousness wondering whether her plan would work.

A rustling in the forest, and then the sorcerer appeared, wearing his wire cape. He set down the basket and extended his arms. "Bird-woman, where is my bride?"

"In the village, preparing for the ceremony," Abena-the-bird said. "I'll carry you across to wait for her."

Abena-the-bird wrapped her arms around him and flexed her wings and her feet left the ground. As she floated over the river she squeezed him tight and whispered, "This'll teach you to hurt Ndidi and Kayin."

His eyes widened as she dropped him. By the time she reached the other bank the sorcerer had vanished, and all that remained was the swirling water, the mortar-and-stone castle on the mountainside, and Ndidi and Kayin bursting out of the basket, shouting her name.

The rest of the summer, Abena spent mornings assembling radios in the basement and afternoons with her sisters: swimming in the river, listening to Kayin's stories by the fountain, and peering in the shop windows with Ndidi. Red highlights appeared in Abena's hair and Ndidi and Kayin no longer sulked or glared at her over supper.

On the last day of August, they walked along the river, near the castle looming on the mountainside.

"You know, I've been wondering," Abena said. "The sorcerer told me he would protect me from dangers. What do you think he meant?"

Ndidi and Kayin said the sorcerer had told them the same thing, but they didn't know what he was talking about.

Abena stared at the castle and an autumn wind blew, hard and relentless. She imagined that someday, perhaps soon, as they marched towards adulthood, she and her sisters would face far worse dangers than a sorcerer in a cursed castle.

She slipped her arms around Ndidi and Kayin's waists. "I'll always protect you," she whispered, and the three of them set off back towards the village as autumn leaves skittered around their feet.

Emily Dickinson takes Helen Keller on a walk in the country
by **Elise Liu**

The clouds fluff up like boiled milk—
The pond—is porridge-thick—
This wind that combs the sapling-grove
Curls boughs—like candle-wicks—

Before us, meadows tumble forth—
Behind, the road retreats—
What fun! But sedge-grass slashes fast—
My dear—do watch your feet—

To right—yes, stretch—a berry-bush—
Whose fruit is sweet and sharp—
The color?—*indigo*—should feel—
Like dewdrops in your dark—

»

About the Poet

Elise Liu is an international development consultant whose work has taken her from Rhode Island exurbs to Addis Ababa, Ethiopia. She has a B.A. from Harvard, where she won the Sosland, Wendell, and Hoopes Prizes for her writing. Her essays and poetry have appeared or are forthcoming in *Thought Catalog*, *The Found Poetry* Review, Humanities, Exposé, and Tuesday Magazine, among others. Elise tweets (@eliseliu), tumbles (eliseliu) and bakes complicated vegan muffins to procrastinate work on her first novel.

Oh—wait—I hear a hornet's buzz—
(*Hornets* are angry bees—
They sound like shivers in the sky—)
Stay still—it's passed!—we're free—

No mind—dear child—put out your hand—
A tickling lady-bug—
Now strides the webbing of your palm—
Uprightly, as it should—

What's that—that warmth? A kiss of sun!
That smell?—A rubbish-heap—
A bit of wool—a wet purse—Oh!—
The stomach—of—a sheep.

Notes:

Emily Dickinson (1830-1886) was a 19th-century poet from Massachusetts whose writings are considered some of the first important works in American poetry.

Helen Keller (1880-1968), struck blind and deaf by fever as a baby, still grew up to become an inspirational commentator on women's suffrage, worker's rights, and other social issues, reading Braille and even learning to speak though she could not hear.

Emily would have been middle-aged when Helen was a small girl.

The Last Khan's Elephant
by Aidan Doyle

THE PALACE OFFICIAL stared apprehensively at the elephant. "You cannot bring this beast in here."

"The holy shining one instructed us to bring the elephant to him as soon as we returned," Tall Khenbish said. The khan was acquiring all manner of creatures for Mongolia's first zoo and had sent Khenbish to purchase an elephant from the tsar. He wasn't sure how an elephant had found its way to Russia, but it was not his place to ask such things.

"His holiness recently acquired a Winton limousine," the courtier said. "He has gone for a drive."

Khenbish glanced at Batzorig, the monk that had accompanied him to Russia. The ruler of Mongolia was nearly blind.

The official cleared his throat. "Two riders on horseback travel ahead of the car, informing citizens of their duty to clear a path for his holiness."

Khenbish, Batzorig and the elephant waited outside the palace gates for the khan to return. A crowd gathered to gawk at the elephant. He lost count of how many times people remarked that the elephant was even taller than Tall Khenbish.

He stood seven feet six inches tall and was widely acknowledged

---

ABOUT THE AUTHOR

Aidan Doyle is an Australian writer and computer programmer. He has visited more than 80 countries and his experiences include teaching English in Japan, interviewing ninjas in Bolivia and going ten-pin bowling in North Korea. —*aidandoyle.net*

as the tallest man in all of Mongolia. The khan liked to boast that the tallest man in the world was on his staff, but Khenbish didn't feel comfortable claiming that title after having visited only one other country. He hadn't seen any Russians that matched his height, but that did not mean there weren't taller Chinese.

It was a cold, crisp afternoon and a light snow was falling. At least it was warmer than Russia. The elephant looked gaunt and haggard after the march south, but it still had that knowing look in its eyes, as if it knew that no one but the rulers of the world could afford to keep such large creatures.

Two hours passed and the crowd eventually dispersed, leaving only a group of children chattering endlessly about the creature's great size. Khenbish and Batzorig watched the line of supplicants shuffling towards the far end of the palace wall, each of them reaching out a hand to touch an electrical cable. After the palace had electricity installed, the khan ordered a cable hung over one of the walls. Hundreds lined up to receive the khan's blessing, which came in the form of a mild electrical shock.

Batzorig spat on the ground. "The time of khans and kings is over. I heard the whispers in St. Petersburg. The Russian people will take control. Mongolia will follow."

Batzorig spoke Russian and had negotiated the terms of the elephant's purchase. Dangerous talk made Khenbish uncomfortable. He just wanted to live a comfortable life.

"You have a big heart," Batzorig said. "You must see the suffering the khan is causing."

Batzorig was a monk, but he didn't seem impressed by the khan's spiritual qualifications. The holy shining one had been born in Tibet, but Mongolia followed Tibetan Buddhism and he had been appointed khan. Khenbish's father had told him that lamas were able to remember their former lives and became wiser each time they were reincarnated.

A horn sounded in the distance and two riders on horseback galloped down the road leading to the royal palace. "Make way," they shouted.

A black automobile roared down the road and squealed to a stop in front of the palace. The khan sat behind the steering wheel, a courtier sitting beside him in the cramped space of the driver's compartment. The courtier's gaze strayed to the elephant standing in front of the gates. It had not seemed at all disturbed by the car hurtling towards it.

The courtier whispered something in the khan's ear and opened the car's front door. "Tall Khenbish, his holiness invites you for a ride."

"Do not say anything about the rumors in St. Petersburg," Batzorig whispered.

Khenbish did not want to be caught up in Batzorig's intrigues, but neither did he want to betray his friend. The khan was ruthless with those suspected of plotting against him.

He opened the car's back door and squeezed himself inside. There was hardly any room for his legs, but he didn't dare put his feet on the seat of the only automobile in the entire country.

The khan wore a driving hat, goggles and gloves. He tooted on the horn and the two horsemen set off down the road, shouting out warnings to clear the way. The car roared after them, horn blaring. Every now and then the courtier would lean forward and gently turn the steering wheel, cueing the khan he needed to turn the car. They were still going far too fast for Khenbish's liking. His stomach churned and he closed his eyes and prayed the journey would be brief.

Officially, there was nothing wrong with the khan's vision. The khan's doctor had unofficially informed the khan's wife that the advancing blindness was the result of the khan's own reckless behavior, but did not provide her any details.

The car slowed to a stop and Khenbish dared to look around. They were on the outskirts of the city. The khan switched off the engine and gestured at the front door. The courtier opened the door and stepped outside, closing the door behind him.

The khan stared at Khenbish with his almost-dead eyes. "How is my lucky pig?" he asked.

Khenbish's parents had both been born in the year of the pig. A shaman had promised them their son would grow up to be big and strong if he was also born in the year of the pig. A family with three pigs was considered the luckiest of all, but it had not been that way for his family.

After the Chinese killed his father, his mother told him he had to leave home. "I cannot keep you," she said. "You eat more than an elephant."

Khenbish was only ten. His younger brother stayed with his mother, but Khenbish was forced to leave home. He would have starved if the khan's people hadn't taken him in.

"What do you think of the Winton?" the khan asked.

"It is most impressive, your holiness."

The khan drummed his gloved fingers on the steering wheel. "Did you hear any rumors when you were in Russia?"

"Rumors, your holiness?"

"About the tsar."

"I cannot speak Russian, your holiness."

"What about Batzorig? Did he hear anything?"

If Khenbish betrayed Batzorig, he didn't think he would see his friend again. But what if the khan already knew Batzorig's views and was testing whether he could trust Khenbish? If Khenbish didn't implicate Batzorig, an unpleasant fate might await him as well. He could not deal with so many unknowns. His father had taught him to count the animals in sight. Strays would have to find their own way home. "I do not think so, your holiness."

"Is he still loyal to Mongolia?"

"Yes, your holiness."

The khan's expression lost some of its intensity. "I knew I could trust Batzorig." The khan asked some questions about the tsar's palace, then they drove back to the khan's palace. The khan did not ask about the elephant.

//

"But I just fed you!"

The elephant looked at him with knowing eyes.

Khenbish sighed. He led the elephant to the palace's small garden and let it strip some of the bark from the trees. The khan owned all of the trees in Mongolia, but sometimes it seemed as though there was still not enough food for his new friend.

At first Khenbish resented the elephant's constant demands for food. It consumed almost 300 pounds of leaves and tree bark every day. But he grew used to its company. Every morning he walked the elephant to the stone fountain in the center of the zoo and gave it a bath. People stopped thinking of Tall Khenbish as freakishly tall when they saw him with the elephant.

Every winter a friend of his father's passed through the city on his way to visit family in warmer climes. He always delivered the same message from Khenbish's mother. Her cows were well, she hoped Khenbish was well and she prayed he would visit her before she died. Khenbish always thanked his father's friend, but said his palace duties meant he was unable to visit his mother. Khenbish missed the openness of the steppes, but like the elephant, he had a long memory.

Batzorig's prediction came true and the tsar was overthrown. The khan forbade anyone from mentioning Bolsheviks. Batzorig fled the city.

The Chinese invaded and placed the khan under house arrest. The elephant pulled a wagon full of bodies away from the palace. The khan was more upset about the confiscation of his beloved Winton.

The Chinese had murdered Khenbish's father, but he was a practical man. He learned to communicate with Mongolia's new rulers and they let him continue to work in the zoo. Even the new Chinese governor agreed there was a certain harmony matching the tallest man in Mongolia with the biggest creature in Mongolia. The governor did insist there were taller people than Khenbish in China, though.

Khenbish learned how to say, "The elephant needs a lot of food," in Chinese.

Then Baron von Ungern and the White Russians invaded. Their artillery shelled the city. The screams of the monkeys in the zoo kept Khenbish awake at night. The Chinese fled Mongolia, and the elephant pulled a wagon full of bodies away from the palace. The khan was freed and Khenbish learned how to say, "The elephant needs a lot of food," in Russian.

The Baron declared he was the reincarnation of the previous khan and pronounced himself joint ruler of Mongolia. Khenbish had always found spiritual matters confusing, but he did not understand how two people could be the reincarnation of the same person. At least the khan did not seem to object too much. He had his Winton back again.

Then the Bolsheviks invaded and executed the White Russians. The elephant pulled a wagon full of bodies away from the palace.

Batzorig returned to the city with a people's revolutionary army and, after negotiations with the Bolsheviks, declared himself head of the interim government. The elephant pulled a wagon full of bodies away from the palace.

"Enemies of the revolution," Batzorig explained. The former monk spent a lot of time dealing with counter-revolutionaries. The only thing that saved the khan was that most Mongolians still venerated the Tibetan lamas.

The khan's wife died and the khan grew ever-weaker, until he was unable to leave his bed. Early one spring morning, a palace attendant summoned Khenbish to the khan's bedchamber. The khan lay on his bed, a gaunt shadow of his former self.

"Is that you, my lucky pig?" The khan's voice was weak and faint.

"Yes, your holiness."

"I heard a family has named their son Melsbat." the khan said.

"I don't know that name, your holiness."

"It celebrates the *heroes* of the revolution. Marx, Engels, Lenin, Stalin, Batzorig." The khan spat each of the names. "Can you believe parents would name their children after those degenerates?"

"We live in difficult times, your holiness," was Khenbish's measured reply.

"I am dying, Khenbish."

Khenbish could not remember the last time the khan had referred to him by name. "I am sure your holiness has many years remaining."

"No, but at least the approach of death has focused my attention. I have done many terrible things in my life, Khenbish." The khan did not give Khenbish a chance to correct him. "I never wanted to be a ruler, but once I took the throne, I did everything I could to keep it."

The khan coughed, a sound that reminded Khenbish of the Winton's engine. "The cycle of birth, death and rebirth is supposed to make us wiser, but sometimes I think we only learn how to be crueler," the khan said. "I had hoped that in my next life I would make fewer mistakes, but the Bolsheviks are plotting against me. They have brought a Siberian shaman to thwart my reincarnation."

Khenbish started to protest, but the khan cut him off with a raised hand. "I am going to transfer my spirit to an animal." He reached out a hand and grasped Khenbish. "Take this animal out on the steppes, far away from the capital. Let me die under the Mongolian sky."

"How will I know which animal, your holiness?" As soon as Khenbish asked the question, he knew the answer.

The khan died two days later.

The next day Batzorig announced that a long search had been conducted to find the new child lama, but the Jebtsundamba Khutuku had failed to be reincarnated. Batzorig declared the People's Republic of Mongolia and assumed the title of Chairman of the Council of People's Commissars.

Khenbish returned to the zoo. When he let the elephant out of its stall, it stumbled uncertainly and knocked against the wall. He peered closer at the elephant and moved his hand up and down in front of its eyes. The elephant had gone blind. The knowing look was gone from its eyes.

"Is that you, your holiness?" he whispered.

It nodded.

The elephant had been the only constant in his life and the khan had taken that away as well. Had the khan spared any thought for the animal's spirit before he replaced it? Khenbish locked the elephant in its stall.

Batzorig had pronounced the khan dead and gone. If they found out he was in the elephant, they would kill it and probably Khenbish as well.

The khan had caused so much harm during his life, why let him cause more trouble? Khenbish knew a trader that would pay good money for fresh meat. He didn't know what elephant meat tasted like, but there would be a lot of it.

His gaze fell on the wagon lying next to the stables. There had already been so much death. Killing the elephant's body, would not help the elephant's spirit. As much as he disliked some of the things the khan had done, the khan had been the only one to take Khenbish in when he was hungry.

He strapped on the elephant's ceremonial armor and attached four bags of food. The khan had spent a fortune on the armor, but had never once ridden the elephant. Even before the elephant had arrived in Mongolia, it had been rendered obsolete by the Winton.

He led the elephant out of the zoo. As he often took the elephant for a walk, the guards did not stop him.

A horn sounded in the distance and the Winton limousine zoomed around the corner. It hurtled along the road towards them. The elephant did not react as calmly to the presence of the automobile as before. It trumpeted in fright and reared up on its back legs, causing Khenbish to scramble away out of the way.

The car screeched to a halt in front of Khenbish. The elephant slowly backed away.

At first Khenbish did not recognize the driver due to the fact that he wore goggles and a driving cap. The driver removed the goggles. It was Batzorig.

"Good morning, Khenbish," Batzorig said. "Where are you going?"

The elephant trumpeted again. Khenbish turned and put a hand on the elephant. "Shhh," he said as gently as he could. Batzorig wouldn't hesitate to kill the elephant if he discovered the presence of the khan's spirit.

Khenbish looked into the elephant's eyes. "Shhh," he said again. "You are in the presence of a very important man."

The elephant seemed to calm down. Khenbish turned back to Batzorig. "Hello, old friend. I am taking the elephant for a walk."

Batzorig frowned. "Does that require the use of armor?"

Khenbish tried not to appear nervous. "The elephant is getting old. The armor had never been worn. I thought it would like to try it at least once."

Batzorig laughed. "You are too sentimental, Khenbish. It is good you stayed in the zoo. The real world is not a place for men like you."

"Perhaps you are right," Khenbish answered.

Batzorig smiled. "Don't worry. Mongolia's future is in good hands." He tooted the horn and sped off towards the palace.

Khenbish and the elephant followed the road leading north out of the capital. At night he slept by the side of the road. It would have been easy for Batzorig and the others to follow him, but the former monk was probably busy dealing with counter-revolutionaries.

The journey was hard work for the elephant. When they passed the cluster of hills north of the capital, the elephant stripped the

trees on the hills of their bark and leaves.

As they journeyed further north, the sky grew bigger. The palaces of Moscow had impressed Khenbish, but the Russian sky had seemed so small compared to the vast blanket that draped itself over the Mongolian steppes. But there were no trees on the steppes and it was difficult to find food for the elephant. Khenbish rationed the food in the supply bags, but the elephant grew weaker.

They finally reached the region where Khenbish had grown up. He asked around and found his way to the place his mother had pitched her *ger*. The sound of a dog barking came from inside the tent. "Hold your dog," he called out.

The ger's front flap opened and an old woman looked out. Her eyes widened when she saw Khenbish.

She looked even more surprised when she saw the elephant.

"How are your animals?" He used a traditional greeting.

"They are well." His mother's gaze strayed again to the elephant. "How are your animals?" she asked in return.

"I was tempted to give away the elephant because of how much it eats," he said. "But I have decided to follow its wishes."

His mother stared up at him. "It has been many years, Khenbish."

A woman holding a baby emerged from the ger.

"This is your brother's wife," his mother said. "And your nephew."

The baby could not have been more than a week old, but it had a knowing look in its eyes.

Khenbish took the baby in his arms. He squeezed its little finger. "Hello, old friend," he whispered.

His brother returned in the evening. Khenbish did not know what to say to his brother, and he suspected his brother felt the same way. Before they ate, he took the last of the food from the supply bags and fed the elephant. Then he joined his family in a meal of stewed rabbit. His mother made sure Khenbish received an extra large serving.

His mother rested a hand on his. She pointed to the elephant eating the last of the dried leaves. "I was wrong," she said. "Elephants eat more than I thought."

The elephant looked tired and weak. The next day he would take it out onto the steppes. He could not think of a better place to die than under the sky's blue vastness.

Intertwining
by Mariva DeBorde

ARE YOU COMING out tonight?
Before the dawn breaks yoke with the sky-
    scrapers?
Will I hasten my ears to hear your gentle
    rapping against my window?

Sometimes I ponder if this is the truth.
Life is a mess,
And intertwining two souls makes it
    worse.

My pulse quickens just sparing you a
    glance,
Your eyes remind me of myself,
Because the reflection I receive only makes
    it clear to me.

About the Poet

Mariva DeBorde is a freshman at Harrison School for the Arts in the Creative Writing Department. She enjoys singing at the top of her lungs, forcing friends into uncomfortable situations, and random trips to Disney World. She drawls much of her inspiration from indie and alternative music as well as reading other poetry and novels.

The grinning against the frigid face of winter,
Staring into the darkness lit with stars together,
My palm sweaty against yours.

You'd say, "stay with me."
And I'd reply, "I wish."
But that wasn't enough.

Your lips pressed me flush against the tree,
That oak tree,
I engraved our names.

This feeling is recognizable,
A foreigner can be identified,
I love you.

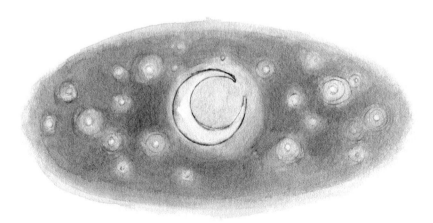

Off the Grid
by Kirt Chris Morris

"I'VE GOT IT," My dad said, waving his phone in the air. I finished chewing a bite of lasagna. "Your phone?"

Dad shook his head. "No, it's *on* the phone. The blueprints for the new Vphone 9."

Ventro is an evil empire. I'm not the only one who thinks so.

Sure, they make millions of people's lives easier with their Vphone home remotes allowing us to turn on the holovision, open the garage, and monitor our security cameras. They even developed a car that can drive itself using up-to-date GPS and Vvision technology. But what society does not know is that Ventro is storing all the info they get—and they place it all in a secret vault.

But as an OffGridder, I value my privacy and work with other members of our secret rebel group work to keep information away from Ventro, their associates, and the government.

I looked at the phone, knowing the importance of the information on the tiny chip inside. "Can I take it to the A-man?" I was almost thirteen, after all; old enough for responsibility but young enough to avoid suspicion. "They won't expect a kid."

Dad looked at me carefully. "You may be right." He tossed me

ABOUT THE AUTHOR

Kirt Chris Morris currently lives in Davis County, Utah, and is the oldest of five children. He has always wanted to follow in his dad's footsteps as an author; his father, Chad Morris, wrote the Cragbridge Hall middle-grade series. This is Kirt's first published story.

the phone and grinned, eyes gleaming. "That is what we're going to have to count on. No matter what, Ventro can't know we have that chip."

"You can trust me, Dad." I slid the phone into my right pocket and waited for my new adventure to begin.

I couldn't help opening the phone while I walked. I looked at the little chip in my hand and felt honored to be trusted and useful. I returned it to my pocket and watched a tube bus fly by, wishing I could travel that fast. My legs would have to do.

A dog bark scared the stars out of me. I wasn't supposed to look jumpy; that would blow my cover. But it was nice to think about something other than letting everyone down if I couldn't deliver the chip safely. But if I could do this, then even Ventro's newest technology could be hacked and wiped off of devices.

I made my way down an empty alley, but began to sweat when I saw the buzzing crowds at town hall. There were cars with Vvision, people with Vphones, security cameras recording all the movement on the street, and pixel sized cameras worn by cops and Vinions.

I took a deep breath, put on my hooded poncho and sunglasses, and followed the path I was taught. I turned the wrong way and found myself in the middle of Mall Square, the busiest place ever. With tons of people hurrying in all directions, all using V's, my hands were shaking like a cold Chihuahua.

I weaved through the crowd, even jogging in spurts before I ducked into another alley. There was a garbage dumpster that was a secret passage to the A-HQ. The A's were the tech squad of the

Ventro is an evil empire. I'm not the only one who thinks so.

OffGridders. They kept us from becoming as backwards as the homeless kids who lived in Dickens's London.

The passageway dumped me out into the lobby but it was eerily quiet. No people anywhere and a big black V was painted on the wall.

Ventro knew about the A.

Did they know about us?

Though horror shook through me, I went to see if there was anything I could salvage in the main office. Most of the drawers were empty, but I found a one of the kidpad chips on the ground. I bent down to pick it up, and just as I slid it in my left pocket I heard the doorknob rattle.

"Freeze!"

I looked up with a jerk. In the doorway stood a big man. The demanding vinion said, "Give me that chip or never leave at all!" Though I couldn't see it, I knew he wore a camera on his coat—all Ventro minions did.

What really puzzled me was how he knew I had a chip.

Scared of being on the grid, me greatest fear, I reached into me left pocket and threw the chip at the vinion, and while he was busy catching it, I jumped into the small garbage can next to the desk entering the tiny emergency exit, waiting to hear the shots behind me. They never came.

I was safe.

I ran back home, not caring as much about being seen as about getting to my dad quickly. Bursting through doors I saw dad talking with another OffGridder on his A-phone. He said goodbye and hung up when he saw me.

"How was your first time?" Dad said with a smile.

I tried to catch my breath, "Dad … Ventro … knows about … the A. I think the A-man … is arrested." And I'm in the database. The vinion surely got a pic of me.

Dad looked shocked. "Were you seen?"

"Nah," I lie. I don't want him to worry.

It seemed to work. He calmed for a second before he asked, "But the chip—what about the blueprints?"

A sneaky smile crawled across my face. "Right here." Reaching into my right pocket, I drew out the little chip. "I told you you could trust me."

Erosion
by **Abby Hall**

I AM THE SAND, and you are the ocean.
Every time we touch, you steal away a piece of me.

I am drowning in you every day of my life;
Your touch, your smell, the way you pull me in and
    push me away.

You are infinite and imposing to me.
Underneath your calm blue are darkness and secrets.

You scare me with your depth, your carelessness,
How you never know when to stop.

I am the sand, and you are the ocean.
Every time we touch, I lose some of myself.

ABOUT THE POET

Abby Hall is a young writer from West Virginia who
enjoys artistic endeavors such as painting, drawing, and
acting when she isn't napping or babysitting.

Starfishing
by Kelsey Dean

a CLEAR, CALM NIGHT with a purple sky is the best kind of night for starfishing. You can't go out on just any old night and expect to catch the elusive shells of stars that lie glimmering under the surface of the water. Stars are like hermit crabs—they live tucked away inside shells, glowing through them and crawling across the sky for hundreds of human lifetimes. And like crabs, sometimes they move into new shells. The old ones fall silently into the sea and settle there, glinting at those who come to gaze upon them in wonder, and twisting away from greedy hearts and hands.

On one such clear, calm night with a purple sky, an old woman lay in an old bed by a window facing the sea. Her rattling breaths interrupted the peaceful darkness, and her eyelids fluttered open despite her weariness. Her granddaughter sat nearby, staring at the ancient quilt that shrouded the frail body without really seeing it. She was lost in the folds and shadows of the blanket; they hid stories of mermaids and pirates, of fishermen, of grandmothers who were young and lively and full of tricks.

Kailani was the girl's name, and she had lived with her grand-

---

About the Author

Kelsey Dean is an adventuress currently living in Istanbul, where she teaches English and arts around in her spare time. She hopes to become either a mermaid or Pippi Longstocking when she grows up. Her work has appeared in an eclectic mix of publications, including *Falling Star Magazine*, *Off the Coast*, and *Vine Leaves Literary Journal*.   —*kelseypaints.tumblr.com*

mother for fourteen happy years full of handmade fishing nets, buckets of clams collected on the beach, and tight braids fastened by steady hands. But lately, Kailani had been braiding her own hair. It was a surprisingly difficult task—her hair was longer and darker than the night, and it was hard to keep it all contained in her hands. She felt tears growing in her eyes as she thought of her grandmother smoothing the thick strands every morning while she sang.

She knew she wouldn't be able to sleep. She was too filled with worry and moonlight and pieces of stories. The sound of strained breathing filled her ears. Her hair was falling out of its neat lines, there were no buckets full of clams, and her father had taken the last of their nets on a fishing expedition. It would be days before he sailed home again. The old woman knew Kailani was awake and worrying, so she turned her face to look at her granddaughter.

"Kailani," she wheezed slowly. "Kailani, look at the night." Kailani stirred and walked over to her. She clasped her grandmother's worn and wrinkled hand and knelt by the bed.

"Yes, Nana, I see the night."

"Kailani, *feel* the night. It is a night for starfishing."

Kailani looked outside, and the starlight filled her with an ache that wouldn't go away. She knew about starfishing. At least, she had heard stories; hushed stories of pulsing lights that swam in midnight waves. The few people who had ever managed to coax a starshell into a net always murmured their secrets to their children and grandchildren. They would stand in the moonlight and recount the story of the capture, watching the waves, floating in their star-spangled memories. Remembering the night it happened made them smile. Remembering the shell itself made them stare into the night, and hold their hearts, and lower their voices to a whisper.

They say on a starfishing night there should be a light breeze, just enough to tickle the hairs on the back of your neck into dancing; there should be a quiet symphony of waves and insects and creaking wood in the air, just enough to caress your ears; and there should be just enough excitement in the water to gently rock your boat. You also need to have your nets ready: no tangles, no barnacles or seaweed. Starshells never really let themselves be *captured*—but sometimes, if the night is right, they let themselves be *found*.

Kailani had heard the softness in the voices of her elders as they spoke of quiet purple nights, but she knew they were just stories. There were no starshells in anyone's pockets or homes. She was sure of that, but her grandmother's face crinkled into a hopeful smile as she gazed fondly at Kailani.

"Yes Nana, I remember your stories. The perfect night for starfishing. There is a breeze, and a quiet symphony, and excitement in the water." She spoke softly and evenly, but there was a tightness in her throat despite the beauty of the night.

"You remember. Kailani, take the boat. Go see the starshells gleaming in the water." The old woman spoke slowly, breathing heavily. She pushed the words out with difficulty as she exhaled.

"No, Nana, I'm staying here with you tonight. I'll stay with you every night."

"I want you to tell me about the starshells, Kailani. Go look at them, so they are fresh in your mind when you tell me. They will glow through your words."

Kailani waited. She did not want to leave the room—she did not know how much longer the rattling breaths would be shaking her grandmother's body. She wanted her to fall into a peaceful sleep. But really, what she wanted the most was to hear all the stories again, in the strong and melodic voice she used to hear every day. She wanted to dangle her feet into the ocean from the dock and mend the nets and strike the scales off of freshly caught fish with her sturdy grandmother like she used to.

"Kailani, there are many things I can no longer do in this old body. But I can listen, and I can remember, and I can see that this night is beautiful. Please, go to the boat."

Kailani looked into the wrinkled face before her and saw the night reflected in dark eyes. She stood suddenly. She would bring light into those eyes again, she thought as she squeezed the withered old hand and kissed a soft cheek. She padded to the door and slipped through it. Her grandmother smiled and turned her face to the window once more.

The night air was warm, and the dock was deserted as Kailani made her way to the boat. Her bare feet dipped into the water, just to feel it on her skin before climbing into the rocking cradle below her. She undid the loops of the rough rope and pushed. She felt calmer already, surrounded by the sea and the night, refreshed by the smell of the salt. She floated away from the dock, the house, the straining lungs and faltering heartbeats; the stars were bright and infinite above her.

Trailing her fingers in the water, she looked over the vast expanse of ocean around her. She could see them, the starshells, winking at her as she passed over them. She couldn't look away, though she knew they were just reflections. They looked like they were dancing, like the hairs on the back of her neck. They were so

beautiful. Her lips were parted, her skin covered in goose bumps, and her eyes seemed to have forgotten how to blink. Eventually, the boat stopped drifting, and she sat placidly among the stars and their fallen shells.

She rested her arms on the edge of the boat, propping her chin on a hand as she gazed at the glittering spots of light that were strewn everywhere, above and below her. Nearby, one reflection seemed to be staring back at her; it was changing, growing. Was she falling into it? Was it coming toward her? She reached into the water—she just wanted to touch it, just for a second. The idea of capturing it had not even entered her mind. It was not something that could just be taken, callously plucked from the place where it belonged.

Her hands were gleaming in the water as the starshell twinkled in her direction. The moment hung suspended in time, and she held her breath, because breathing was just a distraction. Only Kailani, the starshell, and the sea existed.

As Kailani swirled her hands in the water, heart straining with anticipation, the starshell gently nudged her. She soundlessly watched, not daring to move or think; it curled itself into her palm and settled there expectantly. It beamed at her. It was slightly warm, and the warmth of it spread through her hands, into her veins, up her arms and finally to her chest, where it calmed the wild beating of her heart. The radiance filled her to the brim and spilled over in the form of incredulous laughter that drifted away on a breeze. She raised the shell out of the sea, water streaming down her forearms and tinkling back into the calm swells.

She held the starshell high above her head. It was as enchanting and real as each one that still lived in the sky, and she could easily imagine that she had reached right up to the heavens and plucked one like a fruit from a tree. The sky was heavily laden, but she thought that the pieces that fell must be the sweetest and the ripest. She cradled the starshell next to her heart and smiled down at it. It was smooth but lumpy, like the surface of a pearl, and she couldn't quite make a fist around it. It spiraled delicately in a rounded and indistinct shape—it wasn't so brilliant that she couldn't bear to look at it, but her eyes couldn't fully focus on it. She basked in the feel of it in her fingers.

She didn't know how long she sat there, holding the shell; it didn't really matter. But thoughts of her grandmother seeped back into her consciousness eventually, and she pulled the glow away from herself, trying to ignore the sorrow that bloomed inside her as she held it back out over the dark ocean. She felt a chill and a tremor in the starshell as she moved to release it from her hand: it didn't want to go back. Disbelievingly, she pulled it back into the boat, and it warmed up again.

"Can I take you to see my Nana?" she whispered. The shell pulsed with light. Kailani grinned. She nestled the shell in the folds of her skirt and gripped the oars, then dipped them into the sea to guide the little boat back home.

The old woman in the old bed by the window facing the sea heard the soft footsteps of her granddaughter treading down the dock and opened her eyes. Her breathing was as ragged as before, but her eyes were bright and she was eager to hear a story. She smoothed the worn quilt with her old brown hands and smiled at the lovely young girl who glided into the room.

"Nana," Kailani said quietly. "I've brought you something."

"Yes, Kailani, a story. Tell me."

"No, Nana. Not a story. I've brought you a starshell."

She pulled the shell out from behind her back and placed it in her grandmother's hands. The old woman's mouth opened, and for the first time in months the rattling in her lungs stopped. Illuminated by the starshell, Kailani could see the old face regain some of its youth as it bathed in the splendor of the shell.

"Thank you," the old woman whispered.

"Nana, I think it's helping you," Kailani said. "You can breathe again."

Her grandmother tore her gaze away from the shell and focused on her granddaughter. The slim oval of Kailani's face was painted with relief. The corners of her mouth twitched upwards, and her hair framed her features like curtains thrust aside to let light in.

"No, Kailani." The old woman gathered her granddaughter's hands, so that they were holding the shell together.

"But I brought it back for you, Nana! Look, it wants you to be better."

"It's not for me, Kailani. It wants *you* to be better."

"There's nothing wrong with me!"

The old woman's eyes closed and she breathed out slowly. "Not yet," she said. She paused for a moment and studied Kailani's face before continuing. She shook her head sadly as she spoke again.

"Your heart will be hurting much more than my tired body. That's why this starshell let you find it."

Kailani couldn't speak.

"Starshells exist to shelter extraordinary creatures, Kailani. When they are discarded, their purpose does not change. A human heart is not a star, but sometimes a heart needs protection too. This shell is here for *you*. I'm dying; you will need something to warm your heart when I am gone."

"No, Nana, don't say that," Kailani said. The shell glinted between their intertwined fingers, tragically elegant. She knew it was true.

"This shell came on this night to light my way, and to shelter you. Just promise me you'll let it serve its purpose." There was a long pause as Kailani blinked furiously and struggled to find her voice.

"I promise, Nana."

Perhaps minutes later, perhaps hours, the trembling fingers of a beloved granddaughter gently closed the eyes of an old woman wrapped in a quilt of stories. The room was quiet. It was filled with a soft glow from a starshell, and with soft sobs that shook the body of a young girl, and with a gentle whisper from a newly released spirit. The waves outside rumbled, and an old sun-browned and wind-battered shell was left behind as the old soul it once contained soared through the clear, calm night and into the purple sky.

A TV Tube
by Danny P. Barbare

THE ROCK QUARRY. .22 long rifle.
TV tube target. One shot
fifty feet away. It disintegrates.
Father and son. Adventure.
Man. What are you shooting?
A 30.06. Just a .22. Nothing
left but a thousand pieces of
glass. Dad now passed away.
Gun in cedar chest with
World War I German officer
swords brought back from
ransacked houses and hotels.
Mother sold loaded Luger at gun
show. Bayonet and dagger given
away. Browning automatic stolen.

About the Poet

Danny P. Barbare resides in the Upstate region of the Carolinas. His poetry has recently appeared in *Doxa*, *The Santa Clara Review*, *Midnight Circus*, and many other online and print publications. He has two books available: *Gathered Poems* and *Being a Janitor*. He attended Greenville Technical College and is a Member of the National Honor Technical College Society.

for older readers

The stories in this section may be most appropriate for young adult readers—but can be enjoyed by everyone.

Eligible Maidens
by Layla Carr

*e*VERYONE KNEW the story of the Beast.

Ten years ago it had taken up residence in the caves above the village of Aristo, and then stood at the top of the cliffs and made a horrible ruckus—roaring and yelling and stomping its feet until the villagers had fallen to their knees and begged for their lives. The Beast had demanded that in every subsequent year two maidens and two youths be given as tribute, lest terrible vengeance be brought down upon the village.

"It's not that I don't *want* to do it," Athena said, in what she thought was a very calm tone of voice, all things considered. "I'm sure it feels very noble to be sacrificed for the good of the people. I just want to know if there's anyone else who can take my place. You know, hypothetically speaking."

The three bearded councilmen passed around a nervous glance.

"There is no one else," said the oldest and most bearded of them, his voice as high and reedy as a whistle. "You have been chosen by the gods themselves. It is your destiny."

All that sounded rather thin to Athena. She was not the only choice—just the most convenient one. As the niece of Aristo's

---

ABOUT THE AUTHOR

Layla Carr grew up just outside Washington DC in a house that no longer exists, where she received a firm instruction in science fiction, martial arts, and irrational behavior. She currently lives and works in North Carolina, where she enjoys wearing scarves, drinking coffee, and thinking about robots.

witch, she lived apart from the rest of the village. She was not particularly beautiful, nor did she have a heart of gold, nor a smile that could make flowers bloom. A disappointment all around.

"It's not *fair*," she insisted. "I haven't done anything yet! I'm not ready to be eaten."

"To be chosen is a very great honor," the youngest and least bearded of the councilmen insisted.

This is pointless, Athena thought, and stomped away.

The night before Athena and the other sacrifices were to be marched up the mountains to the Beast, she went out looking for someone to help take her out of the running for maidenhood. Unfortunately, all of the village boys had been warned about this eventuality, and told that dire consequences would befall those who attempted to help Athena wiggle her way out of her destiny. She tried her best to threaten one of the younger ones.

"It wouldn't even take too long," she said, hands on her hips. "You'd be home for supper." The boy, grimy and sandy-haired with a crooked nose, stared at her with frozen horror, before bursting into tears.

"Oh, stop that." Athena patted him awkwardly on the head.

She should have been more proactive about it when she'd had the chance. This showed where holding out for true love got you. She thought about running away, but guards were posted at all the gates into town, and it was not as if she had anywhere to go.

At dawn, Athena rose early to prepare. She packed a rucksack with enough food to last for several days. Then she stole quietly into her aunt's workshop, grabbing as many packets of quick-activation spells as she could.

Later that morning, she was marched to the bathhouse where a pair of stony-faced women scrubbed the dirt from under her fingernails and wove flowers into her hair. They laced her into a ruffled red dress.

"I suppose I look good enough to eat," she said glumly to the looking glass.

She was escorted up the mountain path in chains by two village boys she knew by sight but not by name. The younger of them was trembling, sweat beading on the top of his lip.

"It's not as if *you're* going to be sacrificed," Athena grumped, when they were halfway there and still climbing. "And if this is really bothering you so much, you can let me go. I won't tell anyone."

"Don't listen to her," the other boy warned, eyes hard. "She's a witch, just like her aunt."

"I am *not* a witch," Athena said. She yanked defiantly on the chain he held the end of, causing him to stumble and scowl.

"My papa says all women are witches," the trembling boy spoke up hesitantly. "They use their enchantments to force you to buy them new hats and things."

"Your papa is a drunk," Athena responded, not without sympathy.

The mountain path ended at the entrance to the labyrinth, a big, appropriately imposing stone door. It was locked with magic—Athena could smell it. Working in her aunt's shop meant she had grown up around spells. The smell reminded her of having to sneeze—a slight tickling about the nostrils.

The other three offerings were already there, chained together in a line, two young boys and a girl with lustrous blonde hair. Her dress was dark blue, and she was hung with an extraordinary amount of jewelry.

"Nobody gave me jewelry," Athena commented.

The two boys were in loose vests and trousers. Neither of them could have been older than fifteen. Looking closer, Athena saw that they didn't have any jewelry either. That made her feel slightly better.

"Please!" the girl cried as soon as Athena and her captors approached. "Please, have mercy!" She sprang forward, dragging the two youths along with her as she cast herself upon the ground at one village boy's feet. "Release us!" She dug her hands into his waistcoat, clinging on. The boy looked distinctly uncomfortable.

"Let us go," Athena said, figuring it was worth one more try. "I won't tell." She nudged the crying girl with her toe. "She won't tell. You boys won't tell either, right?" The youths shook their heads enthusiastically.

"Can't do it," the older boy—the one with the unpleasant face—said as he chained Athena up with the rest. "This is our job. We'd never live it down if you escaped."

The prisoners were lead to the door of the labyrinth. The two youths looked dismal and the girl was still crying.

"Oh, do shut up," Athena advised her. "It isn't making this any better."

The girl went on crying, tears streaming down her dainty cheeks. Athena raised a hand to slap her. The girl took a quick wheezing breath, tears stopping as if they'd had a plug put in them.

"That's better," said Athena, though her relief was tinged with guilt. She would be crying, too, if she thought it would do any good.

The older boy placed his hand in the center of the labyrinth door. The spellwords he spoke were halting and badly pronounced. Athena thought it was a wonder they even worked at all. With a low, painful creak, the doors swung outward. Inside was nothing but solid, inky blackness.

"Aren't you going to unchain us?" Athena asked the village boys. "The least you could do is give us a sporting chance."

"You aren't supposed to have a sporting chance. You're supposed to get eaten up."

The girl let out a fresh wail.

"Don't worry," Athena said with more assurance than she felt. "I'll get us out of this."

"What could you possibly do?" the unpleasant boy sneered. "Not yet eighteen, and—according to you—not even a real witch." With that, he gave the youth on the end of the chain a rough shove, sending him toppling into the gloom of the labyrinth, the others pulled along behind him.

Athena had been wondering why no sunlight was penetrating into the labyrinth—now she knew. It was because the entrance was a pit, and she and her companions toppled down heels over head. Someone was screaming (Athena hoped it wasn't her), but that came to an end as they landed with a *thump!* onto something soft and yielding. It smelled of magic here, too. A cushioning spell, most likely.

Athena coughed, all the wind knocked out of her, looking up just in time to see the last sliver of daylight disappear as the door shut with a crunch.

"Is everyone all right?" she asked when she had found her voice.

There was movement beside her, then a shaky voice said, "I'm all right, I think."

Another voice whined, "I'm not! We're going to be eaten!"

A third voice chimed in, this one dull and quiet. "It's for the good of our village. It's a privilege to die for our people."

The second voice grew thick and watery. "But we're just children! I don't want to be eaten!"

"Shh!" Athena snapped, her patience fraying. "If you keep making all that noise, we really will be eaten!" She felt around for her rucksack. To her immense relief, neither of her escorts had tried to take it from her. Maybe they hadn't thought it would be any use against a hungry monster. "We need some light." She pulled out what felt like a tiny lump of clay. Standing up, she threw it into the air, yelling out a spellword in a strong, clear voice.

The clay erupted into light, hanging above them like a miniature sun, throwing the labyrinth into eerie relief. Actually, it didn't look much at all like a labyrinth, more like the grand hall of some ancient king that had been stripped of all finery and covered in a layer of dust.

Athena stood up, brushing the dirt off her dress, wishing she had thought to pack a change of clothes. "Alright," she said, surveying her troops. "First things first. Names. I'm Athena."

They stared at her, open-mouthed.

"Come on, quickly now, before the monster comes!"

The girl sniffled. "I'm Marigold."

One of the boys, the smaller and paler of the two, said, "I'm Avery."

"Jason," the second boy said.

Once the introductions were finished, they stood up and endeavored to look around the place that was to become their tomb. Stout pillars held up the vaulted stone ceiling, and any one of them could have hidden the beast. But as it had not yet emerged, Athena did not count it as an immediate problem.

What was an immediate problem, however, was the iron chain that kept them bound together. Maneuvering in a ceremonial gown was already difficult—the chain made it nearly impossible.

"Here," Athena said, reaching into her rucksack and pulling out the handful of spells. They were each labeled in her aunt's precise handwriting. There was one for growing toenails, one for shifting topsoil, two for getting the dust off a piano ... "Here we go, rending! It should have at least four good rends in it. Everybody hold still!"

She stretched the chain out and opened the paper packet. The scent of magic kicked up and the manacle split, falling from her wrist. She closed the packet quickly so as not to release any more of the magic.

"Excellent!" Athena cried. "Hold out your arms!"

She rended twice more just as successfully, but on the third go her hand trembled and she missed her aim. The manacle was sliced off, but the magic also opened a long, narrow gash in Jason's arm.

"I can fix it!" She delved back into the clutch of spells, rooting through them until she found one that was labeled *to heal*. At least, she was fairly sure that was what it said. It might have been *to hear*.

Well, I won't know until I try, she thought briskly. She held the packet over Jason's arm and opened it. The bleeding stopped immediately, would closing up neatly. Jason, who had gone very pale, un-scrunched his face.

"Wow," he said, holding out his arm and staring at it. "You re-

Standing up, she threw the ball of clay into the air, yelling out a spellword in a strong, clear voice.

ally *are* a witch."

"No, I'm not. That's why my aunt makes these spells. They're for people who can't do magic on their own."

Behind them, Avery and Marigold had begun arguing loudly. Athena took a step back to tell them to knock it off, and she accidentally kicked her rucksack, scattering the spell packets every which way across the grimy stone floor.

She cursed loudly, feeling less maidenly than ever. She stumbled after them, picking them up by the handfuls, praying none of them had opened up and spilled out their magic. She was stuffing them back into her rucksack when a horrible roar erupted from behind her, rattling her insides.

Marigold and Avery clutched at each other and Jason cowered against the stone floor, still cradling his arm. The Beast had come.

It stood upright on two thick legs, and its fur was dark and matted and stained with a substance that Athena did not care to know the origin of. When it roared again, its mouth opened wide, revealing two rows of sharp, jagged teeth.

Everyone started screaming again. Athena considered it herself, but irritation quickly won out over fear.

"Stop that!" she snapped. "Everyone making so much noise! Stop it!"

The Beast's roar tapered off slowly, becoming a low, mournful whistle. "But I never have an audience," he said, sounding put-upon.

"Well, then go somewhere else," Athena answered stiffly. "I'm in no mood to be roared at. I've been manhandled and sacrificed all day."

"You're not scared of me?" the Beast asked, sounding more forlorn than anxious. "Not even a little?"

Athena shook her head. "Nope, sorry. You're no taller than a man. And … and no shaggier than a dog, and your teeth are no sharper than a bear's." And then, because he looked so dejected, she added, "But you do have quite a nice roar. But that doesn't mean I need to hear it again!" He had opened his mouth hopefully.

The Beast hung his head. "I never get to have any fun," he said. He shuffled off across the huge room, twisting and weaving, as if he had no idea where he was going.

"You scared him away," Marigold said, awestruck.

Athena shrugged "I just told him the truth. I didn't expect him to take it so hard." The four of them watched as the Beast passed under the arch at the far end of the hall, disappearing into the gloom.

Athena finished picking up the last of her spells and swung the rucksack over her shoulder. She took a step forward, glancing back. The others hadn't moved an inch. "Well, come on then."

Jason shook his head. Marigold sniffed, wiping away a tear.

"There's no way out," Avery said, staring at the floor. "Haven't you heard the legends?"

"Of course I have. I grew up in the valley, didn't I? That's all anyone ever talks about."

"Every year, four must be sacrificed," quoted Marigold.

"No one ever sees them again," Avery added.

"They die," Jason chimed in.

"Well, excuse me if I don't listen to everything I hear," Athena said, squaring her shoulders. "Nobody is going to eat me. Not today, at least. We'll prove them all wrong, won't we, when we show back up without a scratch on us? Come on!"

Athena took two steps forward, before her face connected roughly with something hard and scratchy.

"Ouch!" she yelled, falling backward with a thump. "What was that?"

Slowly, she extended her hands in front of her, until they lay flat against cold stone. There was absolutely nothing to see, but she could feel a wall beneath her fingertips.

"This *is* a labyrinth," she said wonderingly. "The walls are just invisible! That's why the Beast was weaving like that ..."

"But how are we supposed to get out of here?" Marigold asked, her voice scaling up dangerously close to another wail. "We don't know the way!"

"It does make things more complicated," Athena agreed. "We'll just have to spread out and see if we can find the direct route."

This time, there were no complaints. Athena rather liked the feeling of being in charge.

The walls were everywhere, invisible but very solid. Try as she might, Athena couldn't find an opening. The others were not having much better luck. They had employed such useful tactics as jumping up and down or revolving slowly on the spot.

"Oh, this is getting us nowhere," Athena said to herself. "If only I had a spell for something like this."

When she *finally* found a break in the wall, she sprang forward with a cry of victory, only to slam headlong into another one. Around her were similar cries of frustration and pain. One of the cries went on for awhile, and it seemed to Athena that it was coming from above. There was also a great deal of clanking, and above that a constant slithering noise. Athena cringed. She was not a lover of snakes, or anything else without legs.

A small rectangular hole opened in the wall with a grinding groan, and a lump shot out and spun across the floor, coming to rest at Athena's feet.

"Ouch," the lump said, raising its head, which was a mass of dark, tangled curls.

Athena was pleased to realize that it did indeed have legs, and was lumpy only because of a chest plate of armor that didn't fit quite right, and a pack slung over its shoulder. Underneath all of that was a very windswept young man.

"Are you all right?" Athena asked, unbalanced.

"I believe so," the young man answered her, climbing to his feet. His armor was dented in several places, and he clanked whenever he moved.

"Who are you?"

The young man thumped his chest, which made a hollow boom. "I am Zanith the Hero," he said proudly.

"What are you doing here, Zanith?" Athena asked.

"I'm adventuring." He struck an elegant pose, which Athena thought was rather impressive in all that armor. He gave a practiced, albeit clanky, bow. "At your service." He attempted to take her hand, possibly to kiss it. Athena put both of them behind her back.

Zanith looked at a temporary loss, but he covered it up smoothly. "I came to the Purple Mountains in search of a dragon." He had a big voice, and it bounced all around the hall. "To obtain his treasures and rescue whatever princesses he might be holding hostage."

"Well, there are no princesses here," Athena said. "Or any dragons, as far as I'm aware."

"There's a Beast, though," Marigold said, looking immediately shocked that she had spoken. "We're being sacrificed to him."

Zanith appeared delighted at the very thought. He clanked his way over to her exuberantly, giving her a bow even more courtly than the one he had given Athena.

"And what sort of Beast is it?" Zanith asked. "A gryphon, perhaps? Or an ogre? Possibly a sea monster?"

Marigold frowned. "Why would there be a sea monster in the mountains?"

"You would be surprised," Zanith declared, springing up from his bow. "Surprised by the sheer strangeness of all I have encountered! Where does this Beast reside, pray tell?"

"We're not sure," Athena said. "He's somewhere around here."

"He's very hairy," Jason added, "And he spoke well, for a Beast."

Zanith was taken aback. "You *spoke* with it? When? Where?" He looked over his shoulder, turning in an excited circle.

"Gone, for the time being," Athena said.

"You lads fought him off? Well done!" Zanith turned to Avery and Jason, who took a simultaneous step back.

"Not us," Jason corrected. "It was Athena."

Zanith spun on his heel. "Really?"

"I think I may have hurt his feelings," Athena admitted.

"You hurt his feelings?" Zanith marveled. "Then now is the time to attack! His defenses will be down! Well done, Lady Athena! Let us march!"

"Okay. Go ahead."

Zanith squared his shoulders. "Carry on!"

He took a few steps and clanked into a wall, landing heavily on his backside. He blinked a few times.

"I seem to have encountered a setback."

Athena sighed, stooping down and helping him to his feet, which was a much harder process than it would have been without all the armor. "There's a whole mess of walls, all over the hall. That's why we haven't escaped already."

"Ah, yes, invisible walls!" Zanith yelled it triumphantly, like he had just come up with the notion himself. "How silly of me! I knew I saw something that looked like a labyrinth from up above, so you can imagine my dismay when I descended to find nothing but open space. And you lovely citizens, of course." He bent into yet another creaky bow.

"From above … ?" Athena clapped her hands together. "Yes, of course! I can't believe I didn't think of it before!" When all she received was blank stares, she elaborated. "It's magic. Basic knowledge, at least among witches. Illusions require a great deal of power, so it's much easier to maintain them in just one direction. If there is a door that's invisible on one side, it probably isn't invisible from the other. The walls can't be seen from the side, but there's no reason why they should be hidden from above."

Zanith gazed at her with undisguised fascination. "My word … I've never met a witch before."

"I'm not a witch."

"So, that means we could see the walls from up above … ?" Avery asked hesitantly.

"Yes, most definitely," Athena said. "Probably," she amended a moment later. "Hopefully."

"Well, then!" Zanith struck another pose. He seemed to have a few prepared. "We'll simply come at the walls from above."

"But none of us can fly," Marigold pointed out.

"I can," Athena said. Four pairs of eyes settled on her. "I mean, I know a spell for it. It's not really flying, more like . . ." She flapped her arms. "Hovering."

"Oh, good! You really are a witch!" Zanith boomed.

"No, I'm not. But you can't grow up around magic your whole life and not pick some things up."

"Is it in one of your little paper packages?" Marigold asked, waving a hand at Athena's rucksack.

"No, but I know the spellword for it. I just can't do it on myself. Not without a mirror, at least."

"A mirror?" Zanith repeated.

"Magic anchors in the eyes, so I need to be looking at someone to use a spell. That's why you can't perform magic on the dead, or on the sleeping."

"Perform the magic on me, then!" Zanith offered, as Athena had been sure he would. "I will gladly hover above the rest and direct where you need to go!"

"I don't think I can maintain the spell from that far away. I'm not a witch, remember." Athena chewed on her lip. There was a solution, but not one that she liked overmuch. "You'll have to hold on to me. That way, I can do the spell on you, and then keep it up. We can direct everyone from there."

"Why him?" Jason asked. He didn't seem very taken with their unexpected visitor. "Why can't you do it on one of us?"

Athena glanced at Zanith. "He's the only one of you big enough to hold me, I think." Athena had never been dainty.

Zanith was highly pleased with this turn of events. "Why, of course I am strong enough to lift you, my dear lady! All of you, if need be!"

"Just me is enough for now, I think," Athena said. "But you're going to have to take off the armor first. We'll be too heavy if you're wearing all of that."

"But of course, my lady!" Zanith pulled off the dented chest plate, unbuckled the gauntlets, and bent down to unfasten his greaves. It all hit the stone floor with a clatter and a crash. Athena wondered whether the dents had come from actual combat, or just misuse.

Underneath he was dressed in a leather jerkin that had been repaired and patched so many times that it was now a veritable quilt of browns and grays. Even his belt looked like it had been stitched back together. Still, he did look better without the armor on, though less like the heroes in the storybooks and more like the boys who tended the village stables.

"My name is Athena, not 'my lady'. And yes, I'm ready. Look at me, and try not to blink."

Zanith glanced at her for a moment before dropping his eyes to the floor. A very light blush tinted his cheeks. Athena realized that, though he appeared to be very good at bowing and saying courtly things, Zanith was not very sure of himself. That might have been the reason he hardly ever gave anyone else the chance to talk.

"Zanith, look at me," Athena said, as kindly as she could manage.

When he finally did, she saw that his eyes were a very clear grey. She hesitated for a moment, before putting her arms around his shoulders. Then, because he seemed disinclined toward any further motion, she took his hands and placed them around her waist.

"Er …" He hesitated a moment before pulling her against him.

"Don't drop me," Athena cautioned. And she worked the magic.

It stated out slowly, so slowly that at first Athena though it hadn't worked. She was about to try it again, when Zanith let out a squeak of shock, his arms clamping tight around her. His eyes widened. The magic crackled from her fingers, dancing across the patched and tattered arms of Zanith's coat.

"Try no to blink too much," she warned him, and they shot up into the air.

She didn't want to risk breaking eye contact, so she had to more or less guess when they were high enough. She blew out her breath and stopped their ascent, the magic reacting sluggishly to her thoughts.

This would be a whole lot easier if I were really a witch.

Sweat shone at Zanith's forehead, and Athena could feel him shaking, hands trembling against her back. Nevertheless, he was still filled with enthusiasm.

"Excellent, we have achieved our initial objective!" His breath puffed warm on her face. "What now?"

"Now, one of us has to break eye contact long enough to look around."

"Hmmph." Zanith gave a short, jerky nod. "Go ahead."

Athena took a deep breath. She stilled the magic as best she could, anchored it in his eyes, before pulling her gaze away. They wavered for a few moments, dropped a foot or two, before the magic righted them.

"Are we … are we falling?"

"Not yet." Athena glanced down to where Marigold, Avery, and Jason were all staring up. The three of them were grouped at the edge of the hall, from which a meandering labyrinth spread outward. She could only see the walls from above, which made them look more like floating platforms, and her spirits sank as she realized the way was much too complicated.

"It's no use!" she called down. "We'd starve to death before we figured it out!"

Zanith peered over her shoulder. "But no, all is not lost, my lady!" He shifted awkwardly, holding her closer, an arm folding tightly around her lower back to free the other to point down at the labyrinth. "Down there! I can see a way out. If we follow this way, and then curve that way … Yes, it is very possible!"

"Wonderful," Athena coughed, breathing constricted. She was pressed up hard against Zanith's chest, which was slightly embarrassing, but mostly just painful. What's more, all that excited yelling was going straight into her ear. "Just glorious. But can you remember it all when we get back on the ground?"

"Oh … No, I don't think so. Too complicated."

Athena grunted frustration through her teeth. "If only I'd thought to bring something to write with! We could draw a map!"

"A map! Brilliant!" Zanith bellowed in her ear.

"Yes, it is a fantastic idea, Zanith. We just have no way to employ it. Nothing to write with, remember?"

"What? Nonsense—I have all the essential components in my pack."

"Your pack?"

"Yes, that one there." He pointed down to where he'd discarded his armor. "I use them to write up proclamations to read out whenever I enter a town. So everyone knows there is a hero at their service."

"Proclamations?"

"Indeed. I had a herald for awhile, but he was eaten by a vicious manticore in the wilds of Hirdian. Hello, those down on the floor of this terrifying labyrinth! Would you please be so kind as to toss me my pack?"

The three on the floor shared a glance, before Jason hefted the pack up. It barely made it three feet into the air.

"Oh, come on!" Athena called, losing patience. Her muscles were beginning to tremble from strain. "You can do better than that!"

Jason scowled, before picking the pack back up and launching it upward. Athena managed to snatch it out of the air. She held it out to one side.

"Can you get to it?" she asked Zanith. "I don't think my arms bend that way." And it was difficult to do anything while clinging to a body that was bony all the way through. The magic had her as long as she was pressed up against him, but if loosened her grip even a little, gravity would take over in an instant.

"Of course I can," Zanith said, quieter this time. He stuck a hand into the sack, rooting around and pulling out a sheaf of parchment and a stick of oily charcoal.

"Was your herald really eaten by a manticore?" Athena asked, as he shook the parchment out, making them sway dangerously in the air.

His brows pulled in. "Ah, no. Not really. He's at home with the flu. Now go on, draw the map!"

"Me?"

"Yes. I can't draw and hold onto you at the same time."

"Well, I can't draw it and hang onto *you* at the same time!"

Clearly, they did not have enough arms for this.

Athena's head was beginning to hurt from maintaining the spell for so long. Whatever they did, they had to do it fast. "Fine. I'll hold onto you, and you draw the map behind my back."

"Won't the magic release you if I let go?"

Athena grit her teeth. "I'll hold on tight."

"Very well." Zanith let the pack slip from his fingers. "I suppose I truly *am* helping a damsel in distress. Are you *sure* you aren't a princess?"

"Anything is possible, I suppose," Athena said dubiously, voice muffled against his shoulder. "I've never met my parents." She shifted, wrapping both of her arms firmly around Zanith's neck, praying to all the gods she knew that he was hardier than he looked. Sweat trembled at his temples and along his forehead. It must have been from fear of falling, rather than her proximity. She was neither a witch nor a princess—hardly worth getting nervous over.

"Alright," Athena said with grim trepidation. "Go ahead."

All the bracing in the world couldn't have prepared her for the moment when Zanith let go. Gravity settled on her and her feet swung wildly in the air as she clutched at Zanith's back, shouting out a few of her aunt's favorite curses.

"Don't move!" she growled into the curve of his neck, as he began to draw.

"I won't, I assure you!" Zanith sounded uncharacteristically serious. Not distressed, exactly. More as if he had a fully grown maiden hanging off his shoulders.

"I'm sorry I'm so ungainly," she muttered.

"A-Apologies, my lady. But I can't hear what you are saying at the moment. I believe my shoulder is in the way." He shuddered, making Athena swing in the air.

"Stop that!"

"I'm done!" he announced at last. "Let us down!"

This was the bit Athena had been dreading. In magic, getting back was always the hardest bit.

"I need everyone to be quiet," she called.

She did not know how to reverse the spell, so she was going to have to settle for letting the magic escape her slowly, like the wind leaving the sails of a ship. She took a deep breath, locking eyes with Zanith, finding the root of the spell and letting it loose, just how her aunt had taught her. Of course, they had been making pebbles fly and flowers grow, not dangling people in thin air, but the theory behind it was the same.

They began to fall, controlled and slow, but it was falling all the same.

"Excellent," Zanith said soothingly, as they drifted. He had wrapped his arms around her again, bringing her back into the circle of the spell. "We're almost halfway there. You are doing splendidly."

"I know that. Stop talking to me like I'm a horse." No sooner had she spoken than she felt herself lose the strains of the magic. They plummeted the last six or seven feet, landing in a heavy sprawl of arms and legs. Athena gasped as all the breath was forced out of her. The map fluttered down after them, landing on Zanith's back.

"Ouch," Athena said to the ceiling. Her ankle throbbed horribly and she was panting.

"We have returned, my fair friends!" Zanith cried. He attempted to leap to his feet, but his knee twisted and he went back to lying flat on his face. This did nothing to dampen his exuberance. He rolled onto his back and punched lively at the air. "Onward then! Pick up the map!"

Avery pointed. "H-His leg."

Athena was not an expert on knees, but she was fairly certain it was not supposed to bend that way. Zanith had gone the color of cooling ashes, lips drawn tight, but he made no complaints.

"I think your knee is dislocated," Athena said, pushing herself awkwardly to her feet. She looked from his knee, to the pallor of his face. "Doesn't it hurt?"

"A hero must transcend all pain!" Zanith's jaw tightened. "That's what separates the weak from the strong!"

"Yes, well, right now it separates those who can walk from those who have to be carried."

Avery, who was still holding Marigold's hand, asked, "Can't you fix him? You fixed Jason's arm."

"I had a spell for that, and I don't have a spell for knees. We'll have to carry him. Avery, Jason—can you each take an arm … ?"

The boys glanced at each other. They grabbed him around the shoulders. Jason jarred his leg, and Zanith's face went grayer still.

Marigold raised a hand. "Um … Athena?"

"Not right now, Marigold." Athena picked up the map. It was rough and wobbly from being drawn in midair, but she thought she could follow it. She started off walking, tracing her hand along the wall to where an arrow pointed right. There was nothing to see, but a slight draft came out of the space. Turning, she found the opening, wide enough to just touch each side with the tips of her fingers.

The map was surprisingly accurate—Zanith had done a good job. "I think we're almost there," she said after half an hour. The yawning mouth of the hall door was getting steadily nearer, though all the zigzagging was making it take forever. "Excellent map, Zanith," she called back.

"Thank you, m-m lady," Zanith responded. Athena glanced back to find him draped limply between Avery and Jason, face tight with agony.

"I-I'm fine, my—my lady." He smiled wearily. "Onward … onward we go. I want to meet this Beast of yours."

"We can't." Athena's clever plans were unraveling at the seams. "You can't stand, they can barely lift you." She was trying very hard not to look at his knee. The sight of it made her feel like she needed to sit down and take deep breaths. "I don't—"

"Athena … umm …" Marigold stood a little behind Avery, looking pretty and demure and maidenly. "I can … help."

"You can't help!" Athena's frustration frothed up, words striking out like a whip. "Just keep your mouth shut and maybe you won't get us all killed!"

Marigold's lip trembled. She looked at the floor. Then her hands clenched into fists, and when she looked back up, her eyes were blazing and her jaw was set.

"I was only going to say that I know how to fix it! My father is the village physician … so … "

Her voice fell away, leaving an echoing silence behind it. Avery's and Jason's eyes were wide and shocked, and Zanith just looked like he was about to fall over.

"Oh," Athena said after a moment. Her face burned. "Are you sure?"

Marigold nodded once. "Yes."

"Then … um … you fix it, and I'll scout ahead."

Athena was halfway up the steps when she heard a cry of pain, long and anguished. She shivered, feeling like a coward.

The steps were rough hewn stone, made for something with a stride much longer than Athena's. A pattern was carved high on the walls; what once might have been flowers or intertwining vines, but was now nothing but scratches in the stone.

"Who's there?"

Athena yelped. The Beast was standing on the stairs, big clawed hands covering his ears. "Everyone keeps shouting," it complained. It was odd, to see such a huge creature doing something so delicate. "It's making my head hurt."

"I … I …" Athena swallowed. "I'm warning you! Leave us alone … or I'll …"

"*Me?*" The beast dropped his claws from his ears. "*You're* the ones in my labyrinth!"

Athena took a shaky step backward. "I'm a witch! If you eat me, you'll … you'll have indigestion forever!"

She had not expected to inspire much fear with her threat, but neither was she counting on the look of hope that spread over the Beast's fearsome face. "You're a witch? Do you think you—"

"Never fear, fair maiden!" Zanith charged up the stones steps, sword drawn, only limping slightly. "I have returned! Whole and hardy and ready to slay the beast!"

"Stop!" Athena tried to warn as he rushed past her. "Zanith, I don't think you should—!"

The Beast roared, batting Zanith away like a cat with a ball of yarn. He hit the wall with a thud and a clatter, sliding down into a motionless heap of limbs and tousled hair.

Athena rounded on the Beast. "Look what you did! You killed

him!"

"I didn't mean to!" The Beast wrung its claws. "It's just, he had a sword, and—"

"I'm not dead, never fear!" Zanith's response was a little duller than usual, but he sounded like he was all right. That was good. Athena had been frightened for a moment. Still, not thinking before he acted appeared to be a chronic affliction, because he hefted his sword and made another dash for the Beast.

Athena caught him by the back of his coat. "Stop that, would you? It's not getting us anywhere."

Zanith drooped like the fire flowers in her aunt's back garden whenever the sun went behind a cloud.

"Why don't you go make sure everyone's all right?" Athena suggested.

Zanith glanced over his shoulder tentatively. "But you'll be left alone with the Beast. I could never leave a defenseless maiden with a horrible monster such as this!"

"I'm not doing anything!" The Beast's petulant tone was startlingly similar to Zanith's. "And everyone keeps *interrupting me*!"

"Oh, calm down." Athena rounded on Zanith again. "And you! Do you think you can control yourself for half a minute?"

Zanith nodded slowly; the idea seemed foreign to him.

Athena turned back to the beast and attempted a smile. "What is it you want from us?"

The Beast took on a resolved visage. Or as resolved as a tooth-crammed muzzle could get. "Are you really a witch?"

Athena crossed her arms. "No. I lied. My aunt's a witch, I'm just—just an eligible maiden."

"You're also a sacrifice," Zanith pointed out.

"And a sacrifice."

"And you can do spells and things."

The Beast's ears pricked forward. "Spells?"

"I can do *some* spells," Athena corrected. Honestly, mend a few cuts and float someone and suddenly you had all sorts of rumors to contend with. "But I'm not a witch."

"Well …" Zanith tapped a finger to his mouth as he thought, wispy curls falling into his eyes like dandelion fluff. "If the definition of a witch is someone who does magic, and spells are magic …"

"I haven't been to school," Athena cut in quickly. Her aunt had attended school at one of the most widely-renowned magic academies there were. "And you need to do that to be a witch."

"Nonsense!" Zanith protested. "I haven't been to adventuring school, and I do that just fine!"

Athena thought a little adventuring school would not go amiss, but she kept it to herself. "Well, if I can't convince you, I'm not going to keep trying," she said grumpily. "Does it really matter that much?"

"You can use a spell on this Beast!" Zanith suggested with excitement.

"Yes, please do," the Beast said. "I've been down here for such a long time! Please rescue me!"

Zanith and Athena shared a glance. "Come again?" Zanith said.

The Beast stamped his feet, making the entire passage rumble ominously. "I've had this spell on me for such a long time! No one will help. They always just see a Beast and get scared!"

"Well, you can't exactly blame them," Zanith reasoned. "I mean, you do eat them."

"What? I don't *eat* them! Who told you that?"

"She did." Zanith pointed at Athena. "I was just looking for dragons to slay."

"I—I'm not really sure who *told* me," Athena admitted after thinking on it for a moment. "I suppose I just always knew. Everyone in Aristo does. The Beast demands two maidens and two youths every year."

The beast rolled his yellow eyes. "I never demanded anything. I roared a lot. There may have been a misunderstanding. Then they just started sending people up. Hordes of them! I could never get any sleep."

"*Misunderstanding*? How can you misunderstand the intent to eat someone?"

Zanith brought his sword back up, getting his second wind. "Yes! And you are a Beast! That's what Beasts do!"

The Beast turned his very disapproving glare on Zanith. "Stereotype! Besides, I haven't always been a Beast. I was a human."

Zanith wavered. "What?"

"What happened?" Athena asked cautiously. It sounded like a rather Beast-like trick to try.

"A wizard. At least, I think he was a wizard. He dressed like one."

"How do wizards dress?"

"You know." The Beast made an ambiguous motion with one of his massive paws. "Fancy."

"What did you do to him to deserve this?"

"Um ... I'm not really sure. I was new in town. I come from Belkinor—"

"That's where I'm from!" Zanith announced happily, in a momentary burst of camaraderie.

The Beast glared again at the interruption, but then went on. "I didn't know the customs. I may have insulted his mother. Or turned down a marriage proposal. I'm not sure which. Anyway, he turned me into a Beast and imprisoned me here."

Athena crossed her arms. "If you didn't eat them, what happened to all the other sacrifices?"

"They left."

"Left?"

"Yes, left." He waved a claw up the winding steps. "There's a way out up there. I'm just too big to fit."

"Really?" Athena felt lightheaded with relief. "But—" She turned back to the Beast. "If they got out, why didn't they ever come back? We never saw any of them again."

"How should I know that?" the Beast asked. "*I* couldn't follow them."

"Perhaps they didn't want to go back to the village that sacrificed them," Zanith suggested. "I imagine that could make one lose faith in one's community."

"Change me back!" the Beast implored. "Undo what the wizard did! Please! I've been alone for so long!"

Athena considered reiterating she wasn't a witch, decided it was useless, and instead said, "I don't know how to do that sort of spell, I . . ." She trailed off. "I need my pack!"

She flew back down the steps, leaving Zanith staring blankly after her. Jason, Avery, and Marigold were grouped nervously at the foot of the stairs. Athena waved their questions aside, diving for her pack and hoisting it up on her shoulder. She sprang back toward the steps, treading on the hem of her ceremonial dress and nearly tearing it.

"What's going on?" Jason called after her, but she ignored him. She dropped her pack when she reached the landing, unbuckling the straps and delving down into the spell packets. She gave herself a few paper cuts before emerging triumphant.

"I knew I'd seen that in here!"

The little paper packet looked just like the others. The word *monster* was written across it in her aunt's looping handwriting.

"I think . . ." She passed the packet between her fingers. "I think this might work."

"What is it?" the Beast and Zanith asked at the same time.

"One of my aunt's spells. See, you can't cast the same spell on someone twice. They won't intensify, they'll just cancel each other out." She brandished the packet. "So if this is the same spell that the wizard used on you, it should turn you back."

The Beast eyed it warily. "What if it's not the same spell?"

"Then you might turn into another type of beast. A dragon, maybe. I'm not sure."

"A dragon?" Zanith looked hopeful.

The Beast gave a rumbling sigh. "I suppose it can't get any worse."

Athena stepped in closer, unsure of the range of the spell. She wanted to at least be far enough away to jump back if things went wrong and a dragon happened.

Here goes nothing, she thought, and opened the packet.

Smoke billowed out, followed by a shower of sparks and some alarming popping noises, along with roaring and the stomping of enormous feet. Athena leapt backward, nearly treading on Marigold. The others had appeared on the steps behind her, drawn by all the commotion.

"Did it work?" Zanith asked, when the popping finally subsided and the smoke began to drift up the stairs.

The Beast was gone. In his place was a pale, shaken young man. He had a mop of dark curly hair, and a very familiar face.

"Hey," Avery said from behind. "He looks just like …"

Zanith's mouth was hanging open. "*Hareth*?"

The young man's eyes widened in surprise. "Zanith?"

"What …" Athena stared as Zanith let out a whoop and embraced the boy.

"I don't get it," Jason said.

"This is Hareth!" Zanith exclaimed. He hugged the young man again. Hareth grunted as Zanith knocked his chin against his shoulder blade. "My brother!" Zanith beamed. "He's been missing for more than ten years! We always thought a gryphon had carried him away! You don't look a day older than when you left," he said to Hareth.

"Really?" Hareth asked, scratching his head. "That's strange."

"I imagine he didn't age while he was under the spell," Athena said. "That's also most likely how he didn't starve to death."

Hareth pulled out of the circle of Zanith's arms. "I'm sorry I didn't recognize you before—you're much older than when I left, and my eyesight wasn't very good when I was beast."

"That's quite alright!" Zanith said happily.

"Um …" Marigold spoke up from behind them. "Did someone say something about a way out?"

"Yes! Finally! It's just up these stairs!" Hareth beamed. "Zanith, are these your friends?"

"Ah, yes, of course. How rude of me! May I present Masters Avery and Jason, and the Lady Marigold, and La—Athena. She's a witch," he added.

"I'm not—" Athena shook her head. "Nice to meet you."

"Likewise!" He swept into a bow just as courtly as his brother's. "Now, let us escape!"

They sprang up the stairs, and Athena hung back a little on purpose, until she was beside Marigold.

She cleared her throat awkwardly. "I-I'm sorry for earlier," she said. "I was very rude."

"It's okay," Marigold said graciously, smiling in a very maidenly way. "To be fair, I was screaming quite a lot."

Relived, Athena hastened to catch up with Zanith and Hareth, who were discussing the best methods for avoiding entanglements with wizards.

"Oh, hello, Athena," Zanith greeted cheerily. "Glad to be going home to your village?"

Athena wrinkled her nose. "I don't think I'll go back. They might just try to sacrifice me again, somewhere else. And besides, I've always wanted to see the world. Have adventures."

"Well, that's what we were planning on doing," Hareth said, as they began to see daylight. "You can come along if you'd like."

"Perhaps." Athena did not want to pledge herself to anything yet. Rounding one last curve, she let out a gasp of excitement as they came upon the crack in the cavern wall. There was just enough room to squeeze through.

"You know," Athena said. "Hareth should go first. He's been trapped here the longest."

"Yes, I quite agree!" Zanith prodded his brother in the ribs. "Go on, Hareth!"

Hareth's smile grew by degrees, edged with disbelief as the sunlight touched his face. Athena found herself smiling along with him; she could not imagine spending a decade in this miserable place. After that, she and Zanith both stood aside to let the others go ahead, Jason shielding his eyes against the glare, Marigold and Avery only releasing each other's hands for as long as it took them to scramble through.

"This all worked out well," said Zanith.

"*Too* well. Next thing you'll be telling me I really *am* a long lost princess."

Zanith squinted at her. "Well, you do look a great deal like the Queen of Kosela, now that I think on it. Her daughter has been missing for seventeen years."

"*Don't* tell me that," Athena warned. "I've been an eligible maiden, a sacrifice, and a witch all in one day. I don't think I could handle being a princess as well."

"I think you'd make a much better princess than sacrifice," Zanith said graciously. He leapt nimbly through the crack in the rock, turning back and offering her a hand, the sunlight turning his hair into a fuzzy halo.

Before she could even think about refusing, Athena took his hand and let him pull her up to join the others. The wind was warm, the perfect blue of the sky marred only by the distant haze of chimney smoke rising from Aristo. Together they turned away from the village and the cavern, looking out onto a countryside that was clear and bright, brilliant with possibility.

An Herbwife Lives by the Dragons' Eyrie

by Bethany Powell

"I'LL LACE YOU BACK up with this sliver of bone
—these dragon-torn edges will heal to nice scars
with this spur of swan's wing blessing it in stitch
and a packing of fresh-crushed herbs.

"This little cottage of slate and thatch
has watched heroes pass and few get back
so I dread to see them coming,
dragging their bodies back over that ridge.

"Your gaping long gashes look handsome, compared
to the state of most I've tended here.
Those who haven't won their first attempt don't try
again
so sometimes I have to wonder if they lived."

》

ABOUT THE POET

Bethany was born in Boston, spent her teen years in rural Japan, and now lives in Oklahoma. It doesn't explain everything, but it explains a whole lot. Her fantasy poetry is largely inspired by the weird bits of country life that don't make it into many stories.

—bethanypowell.com
Twitter: @oh_gingersnap

Wait. I recognize this scar—it's two, three years old.
But he—he had a child's face then, and tears.
This mighty burn I fought to keep clean and bare
—and his mind from shattering with pain.

He asked me, when he could walk again
"Why do you live in this place?" and was the first.
"Because my father died on his journey home
from a bite gone fetid, despite his win," I said.

I'm stunned he lived—and how did he dare return?
"So. I remember this trophy on your side.
You look quite different now. I'm glad to say.
You have no dragon's tongue, but you also lost no legs?"

Those eyes—one night he's going to escape
and try even another time. So he's remembered me?
"Vengeance, for your father, too," he says.
Romantic, still, then, and with a fuller jaw to—kiss?

Not the first time someone's tried, my recoil is a habit.
But now I will be tasting the passion that drives him,
bitter as the yarrow I've made him drink,
and think of him coming back for both of us.

"Don't think I'm fooled by that hobbling.
I saw you rewrapping your knife's long hilt.
I've made up a chicken for you, guessing
that you'd try again so soon."

This mouth, it belongs close with mine.
The saltwater sting in my traitor eyes
won't be seen if he will keep me this near.
All night? No, he's going to go now.

"I will bury your burnt bones under a grape vine, you ingrate.
They say ash is good to mulch them.
All I have left is this morbid humor,
I built my house by a dragons' den.

"I have buried so many heroes.
And so many needles I broke in their skin.
You know what I've done for their burns and bites—
I've never learned to expect them to win."

There isn't a sadder sight than such shoulders
dropping out of sight over the edge of the eyrie.
He asked a hard question, back then—Why do you stay?
"Because I hope you'll come back, all the same."

The Protectors
by P. Jo Anne Burgh

I DON'T WANT to find the boy.

Truth be told, I don't even want to look for him. Hadn't been for Jake hounding me, I'd be sitting at home in front of the fire, playing checkers and pretending Jake wasn't cheating. Instead, I'm out here in cold rain and mud, with my soggy little brother leading the way up a trail so narrow it don't even deserve the name. I don't know what's worse, Jake's chatter on normal days or his quiet now. He ain't said more than three words since we left town.

He knows what's gonna happen if we find the boy.

Everybody knew Amos Parker was mean as a snake. I had occasion to tangle with him a few times myself. Got the bite marks on my hand to prove it. Danged if I know how Mary Beth Simpson got herself messed up with him. He was as ornery a fellow as I ever met, and she was right pretty when the light hit her just so. But I reckon a gal can do dumb things if she wants to, and this one was a doozy. Next thing everybody knew, there was a shotgun wedding and little Tommy Parker.

Tommy and Jake went to school together. That's partly why Jake's

---

ABOUT THE AUTHOR

P. Jo Anne Burgh is a Connecticut lawyer. Her short stories have appeared in *Spark: A Creative Anthology*, *On the Premises*, and *Bethlehem Writers Roundtable*. She works best with classical music in the background and a cat sprawled on her desk. She is working on her first novel.

all het up about finding him now. Him and Jake never did much together, but my little brother used to keep an eye out for him anyhow. Sometimes Jake'd come home, all bruised and bleeding, and he wouldn't say why, so we figured he'd just been in another fight and Pa'd give him what-for about not holding his temper. Wasn't 'til today Jake told me how he'd gotten so beat up back then. Seems Tommy'd come to school looking near as bad as Jake did when he got home, and the kids made fun of him. My hotheaded little brother wasn't ever gonna sit still for that. So, he'd jump in and try to stop it. Since he's always been one of the littlest kids in his class, he never came out of it too well, but he tried anyhow.

I never knew any of this before today. Jake never said a word. Tommy made him swear on the Bible he wouldn't tell anyone. Tommy said if Jake talked, things'd be worse. So my little brother gave his word and never backed away from it, not even when Pa tanned his hide for fighting.

Me and Jake were in town when we heard the news. We were just about done loading the wagon when Ida Mae Wilson came running down the street, screaming and wailing, "She's dead, she's dead!"

I caught her arms and made her face me. "Who's dead?" My voice was harsh and loud. I don't usually take that tone with ladies, but I needed her to hear me. Jake crowded in beside me to get the news.

"Mary Beth Parker!" Mrs. Wilson screeched.

My little brother whispered a word I knew he never heard from Pa. If I hadn't had my hands full with Mrs. Wilson, I'd have marched him right back to the wagon then and there, and that would have been the last time he'd have been sitting down for some time. Saying something like that—and in front of a lady, too. But before I could do more than start to turn his way, he was off like a jackrabbit, running down the street toward where Mrs. Wilson came from. A crowd was starting to gather around us, and I lost sight of him, what with Mrs. Wilson crying and everybody jabbering and getting in the way.

It took a few minutes before Sheriff Anderson got there, and a few more before he had the story. By the time he got rid of the crowd, and him and me was heading down the street to the Parker place, probably ten minutes had passed since we'd met up with Ida Mae Wilson. An important ten minutes, as it turned out, but we couldn't have known it then.

The Parker place ain't much to look at. Amos was always more interested in the inside of a bottle. But when we got inside, it was pretty clear things had been a lot worse than anybody knew. There was blood everywhere, and a broken whiskey bottle on the floor. Somebody'd smashed off the bottom the way you'd do to make a weapon. They'd made a fine one, too. Mary Beth had been pretty much cut to ribbons. I closed my eyes. She was a nice girl. She deserved better.

Then I heard a groan. In the corner, looking for all the world like a pile of bloody rags, was Amos. A knife was sticking out of his gullet. He was bleeding like a stuck pig, but he was alive.

Efraim Anderson hustled over to the corner. Amos' eyes were barely open. "Amos! Amos!" The sheriff slapped his cheek to try to wake him up. Over his shoulder, he said, "Go get Doc Higgins." I ran out the door of that sad little house and up to Doc's office as fast as I could, but when we got back, Efraim was shaking his head. "Too late."

"Did he say who done this?" I asked.

"Nope," said Efraim. "Jest kept askin' for his boy."

That was when I remembered Jake. I didn't know where he'd gone in such an all-fired hurry, but wherever it was, I was glad he was there and not here. He might be all of fourteen and doing a man's work on the ranch, but there's still some things he ain't old enough to see.

We waited with Mary Beth and Amos until the undertaker got there. On the way out, I said to Efraim, "Lemme know if you need me for the posse."

"What posse?"

I pointed my thumb back at the Parkers'. "You ain't gonna look for whoever did that?"

"What makes you think they didn't kill each other?" Efraim asked. I allowed as how it made sense. I figured he likely knew a lot more about what went on in that house than I did. Then he said, "Thing I wanna know is, where's the boy?"

I was ready to say I didn't know anything about that when it dawned on me I just might. So I got myself away from Efraim and started combing the town for Jake.

I found him at the livery stable, currying one of the horses. No surprise there. If you can't find Jake, look for the nearest horse. In a few years, it might be the nearest beer, or the nearest pretty gal, but for now, it's still horses. "Where in tarnation you been?" I thundered in my roughest voice. He looked up, and right away I wished I hadn't shouted. The kid looked like he'd been scared half to death. I could see the tears in his eyes. He moved toward me, into the light, and that's when I saw all that blood on him. I knew right then that he knew more about what I'd just seen than I did. A lot more.

"You okay?" I waited 'til he nodded. Then I wrapped my arms around my little brother in a too-late effort to protect him from knowing such hurtful things. He felt so skinny, like a stick I could break with one hand, and he held onto me and cried like he hadn't since he was six. I let him get it out. I knew I was going to have ask him some hard questions, and I was going to have to make him answer, but not yet. I needed to know about Tommy Parker, but my brother came first.

When Jake was quieter, I took him into an empty stall and sat him down. I closed the stable door so we'd hear if anybody came in. Then I sat down next to him. He didn't look up. I lifted his chin so he had to look at me. "We gotta talk," I said. I let go of him, and his eyes slid back down to the floor. Pa would have made him look up to show respect. I didn't care about that right then. I was more worried about getting a straight answer out of him.

I figured I'd start with the obvious. I pointed to his shirt with all that half-dried blood. "Where'd that come from?"

"Parkers'."

I could barely hear him. He closed his eyes like he wanted to hide forever. "Jacob," I said, and he looked up at me in a way that just about broke my heart. I made myself be tough. "Now you listen," I said. "I'm right here, and everything's gonna be all right, but you gotta talk to me. You gotta tell me what happened. All of it."

At first, he didn't say anything. Then, just when I was going to get strict like Pa, he started to talk. He told about Tommy and his pa, and about the fights at school and how Tommy'd made him swear on the Bible not to tell anybody. "I almost told Pa once, but I couldn't," he said. "I gave my word." I was torn between being proud of him for keeping his word even when it meant he got in trouble, and being mad at Pa and me for doing too good a job at teaching him how important that was. It never crossed our minds to tell him sometimes he should break his word.

"When Mrs. Wilson said Mrs. Parker was dead—where'd you go?" I asked.

"Parkers'."

"Why?"

"'Cause—I was afraid."

"Of what?"

"Of what he might do to him," Jake whispered.

"Was Tommy there when you got there?" I asked. Jake nodded. "What happened?"

"It was all happening so fast—he had that big knife—and she was layin' there, and there was blood everywhere, and he said he was gonna kill him—" The boy was shaking so hard. I held him tight. "They fought—and he stabbed him—I saw him do it—" His breathing got faster and harder, and I held him closer.

"It's all right, it's over now," I said, real quiet, like he was a wild thing. Watching his friend get stabbed—I couldn't even imagine it. Eventually, he quieted down, and we sat there for a while, not saying anything.

Then I had a thought. If Tommy'd been stabbed, why wasn't he at the house? "Jake?" The boy barely looked up at me. He was so worn out, he'd almost fallen asleep. "Jacob. Where's Tommy now?"

That woke him right up. He sat up straight and moved away from me. Damn. Whatever I heard, it was gonna be bad. I asked again: "Where's Tommy?"

"I can't tell you," Jake whispered.

"You gotta," I said. "That boy's hurt. We gotta find him, get him some help."

"What d'you mean? What happened to him?"

I was confused. "You said he stabbed him." But Jake shook his head, and then I knew. "You mean—"

He nodded. "Tommy did it. He stabbed his pa."

Oh, sweet Lord, no. "You gotta tell me where he is," I said. "The sheriff's gotta get out lookin' for him." *And bring him back to stand trial.* "Where is he?"

"Uh-uh," said Jake. "I can't tell you. If they bring him back, his pa'll beat the daylights out of him. That dirty ol'varmint already killed his ma 'cause she was gonna leave. He'll tell 'em Tommy did that, and if Tommy don't hang, he'll do the same thing to Tommy he did to his ma."

That was when I realized Jake and Tommy had left that house too early. They didn't know how things had turned out. I placed both hands on Jake's shoulders to hold him steady. As gentle as I could, I said, "Jake—Tommy's pa died."

Jake turned sickly white. He bolted from under my hands and didn't get quite to the door before he was on his knees getting sick. When he was done, I helped him to his feet and kicked some straw over the mess. We went back to the empty stall and sat in the hay for a while, Jake leaning against me. One of the horses nickered, and another snorted. Neither of us said anything. Finally, I said, "We should get going. Pa's gonna be wondering where we are." We'd stop at Efraim's office first and tell him what Jake saw. He'd take it from there.

But Jake stared at me like I was loco. "We can't go home," he said. "We gotta go to Tommy."

"What?" First he didn't want anybody going after the boy, and now he did. Something didn't add up.

"Gus, we gotta go after him." Jake was getting frantic. "There's gonna be a posse out lookin' for him. We gotta get there first. We gotta help him get away."

"Whoa, Little Brother, slow down," I said. I didn't tell him what Efraim had said about the Parkers killing each other. Nobody knew yet they had reason to look for a killer.

But there'd likely be folks searching all over town for a boy who just got orphaned, and if they found him all bloodied up like Jake was, somebody was bound to start asking questions. I knew Tommy was good at keeping his mouth shut—he'd been doing it for years—but I also knew once word got out, it wasn't going to be about an orphan any more. Pa for one wasn't going to stand by and do nothing, not after his boy had seen a man get murdered.

Pa's been on the town council for almost three years now, and he has a powerful strong belief in law and justice. Even if that belief was gonna have to do fierce battle with the part of him that has his own fourteen-year-old boy, I couldn't see him and the council letting Efraim not follow the law. And once they found Tommy and slapped a murder charge on him, I didn't know if being a kid would keep him from the noose or not.

"Gus, please, we have to go after him, we have to help him, we just have to, I promised him that it would be all right, we have to help him, please, Gus, please." Jake was panicking. *Oh, Lordy.* There was something else I didn't know. I could just feel it. And I knew I wasn't gonna like it.

I took the boy by both arms. "Stop," I said. "Just stop." Jake stopped talking, but he was still shaking. I looked him straight in the eye. "Jacob," I said, using Pa's strict voice. "What did you do?"

Jake's eyes widened. He seemed almost scared of me, which was good. I needed him to be worried enough to tell me the truth, not some Jake-version of the truth. His eyes darted around the empty stall we were sitting in. At first, I thought he was trying to avoid telling me. Then, I knew.

"Did you get him a horse?" Nodding. "A horse from here?" Nodding again. "How did you pay for it?" He shook his head.

I closed my eyes. Tommy was a killer, and he stole a horse—and my little brother helped. I knew there was some fancy name for what Jake did, helping out with a crime. Pa would know the word. He'd know what to do, but I didn't. This wasn't some kid prank. This was as serious as serious gets.

"Listen to me," I said in my rough voice. "Did Tommy say where he was going?" Jake bit his lower lip. He looked at me, then down at his boots. I shook him, and he looked up again. "Where was he going?"

"I can't," he said. "I promised I wouldn't tell."

I let go of him then. I sat back, and I tried to explain to my little brother how sometimes, the best thing you can do for somebody is break your promise. He kept nodding while I was talking, so I knew he heard me. But then he said, "So, was I wrong to keep Tommy's secret all this time?"

I didn't know how to answer him. If I said *yes*, it would be like saying this whole awful day was his fault and if he'd spoken up sooner, Tommy's folks wouldn't be dead. Maybe that was so, and maybe it wasn't. There was no way to know. But if I said he wasn't wrong then, how could I convince him to break his word now?

"You did the best you could, Little Brother," I said at last. "But things are different now. You gotta tell me where he is."

He shook his head. "I said I wouldn't tell," he said, as Jake-stubborn as ever. Just when I was about to grab him and shake him hard, he added, "But I didn't say I wouldn't show anybody."

I breathed a big sigh of relief. "All right, then. Let's go get Efraim, and—"

"No!"

"Jake, he's the sheriff, he's gotta go—"

"No! Just you an' me, nobody else!"

I blew out my breath. "You ain't goin' no place but home, Little Brother," I said.

"I said I'd show you," Jake said. "If you don't take me, how'm I gonna show you?"

My head was pounding by this time. "All right," I said. "Let's just head out to the ranch and get some supplies and tell Pa, and—"

"No!" It was almost a scream. "Just you and me! Nobody else! They won't understand!"

He wasn't making any sense. I was almost afraid to take him out of there. He'd had such a terrible, terrible day. Part of me wanted to leave Tommy Parker to his own devices and take my little brother home to sit in front of the fire so Pa could make everything all right. I could hear the rain that had started up while we were sitting here. I didn't know how I'd ever explain it to Pa if I took Jake out looking for Tommy with Jake in such a state.

Right then, I hated the whole Parker family, and Amos Parker most of all. It ain't like me even to think such a thing, much less say it, but for that second, it was true. Seeing what they did to my little brother, with all their secrets and beatings and bloodshed—if Jake hadn't been so desperate, I think at that moment I just might have wished Tommy luck and taken my brother home where he belonged.

"Gus." His voice was so quiet. Those big blue eyes were shiny with tears. "Please."

It went against everything I knew I should do, but I couldn't say "no" to him. He'd been through so much, today and for years before today. He needed to finish what he'd started, or it would haunt him forever.

"All right, here's what we're gonna do," I began. "I'm gonna tell

Efraim what we're doin'—yes, I am," I said, staring him down as he was about to fight me on that. I'd let Efraim take care of talking to Pa. "An' then I'm gonna get us some horses and supplies. Meantime, you're goin' over to Daisy's, and you're gonna get something to eat, and you're gonna take a rest. I ain't gonna have you tumblin' out of your saddle 'cause you're fallin' asleep on me." I knew I could count on Daisy to keep quiet. Me and her grew up together. She ran a little restaurant in town, and she made the best gooseberry pie I ever ate. More important, she knew when not to ask questions.

"I ain't tired," Jake protested. I ignored him. The boy was plumb worn out. I'd have left him to sleep right there in the horse stall if I'd been convinced nobody would come by, but it was too big a chance. Besides, I didn't want anybody thinking of Jake when they were trying to figure out what happened to one of the horses.

"Come here," I said, standing up. I rolled up his sleeves and put my vest on him. It wasn't much, but at least it covered most of the blood.

As we started to leave the stall, I had a thought. I fished two bits out of the vest pocket and laid it on the divider between this stall and the next one. At Jake's look, I said, "That's for Tommy's horse."

"Thanks, Big Brother," he whispered.

I laid my arm around his shoulders. "It's gonna be all right," I said, just like I had any reason in the world to believe I was telling the truth.

We've only been out here a couple hours, but daylight's fading fast. Maybe I let Jake sleep too long, but he needed it so. I almost didn't wake him, but I thought of Tommy, all alone in the world, sleeping out in the rain, and I knew we couldn't let that happen if there was a way not to.

As soon as I touched Jake's shoulder, he sat bolt upright. Most times, it takes a team of mules to get that boy out of bed. My heart hurt to see the look in his eyes. If I hadn't promised him, I'd have taken him right straight back to Pa. For a second, it almost struck me as funny—both of us tangled up with Tommy Parker on account of promises we made that wiser people would have told us we shouldn't keep. But it was too late now. We were going.

All Jake said when we were leaving town was to head west. I didn't ask, but I wondered if Tommy was hiding on our land, because west from town takes a man straight across the Bar J. Sure enough, we've been on Robinson land for more than an hour. I'm trying not to think about what's gonna happen when Pa finds out I had Jake out tracking down a killer on our own land. Somehow, it don't seem as bad if we're someplace else.

When we got to the split in the road, the one that leads up into the high country, Jake said, "I'll lead from here." Something in his voice, and I knew not to argue. So I dropped back, and he took the north fork and then right off the road, along some pretty narrow paths that we had to fight the horses to get through, and up this trail we're on now.

We're going slow, but I'm watching Jake enough to know he ain't tracking Tommy. Not that he couldn't if he wanted to. Even with the rain washing away the main part of the trail, there's enough broken branches and tracks on the edge to see that somebody came through here not long ago. Anybody could follow these signs without half-trying. But Jake's just riding, which means he knows right where Tommy is. Which means they planned this, Tommy and Jake. Mainly Jake, 'cause Tommy's a town boy. There's no way he could figure it out, not this trail. At some point, him and Jake must have made this ride. The thought makes me go cold. Once upon a time, Tommy Parker and my little brother knew a day like this would come along.

We're climbing higher. I know where we're headed now. There's a cave not too far from here. I played there when I was a young'un, and so did Jake. Sure enough, when we come around that last curve, there's a little bay mare tied under a tree. You can't see the cave mouth from here, just the rock side of it. It hits me for the first time that Tommy and Jake must have meant all along to meet up here. I don't know what they figured they'd do next, whether Jake was going to ride with Tommy a while or what. I'm sure my little brother never thought about the peck of trouble he'd be in when he came home after disappearing without a word. That's so much like him. He jumps in to help, and hang the consequences.

Jake reins in his horse, but doesn't dismount. He looks back at me. Before I can speak, he holds a finger to his lips. We sit quiet for a minute, listening. There's no sound but the rain that's coming down hard on the branches, on our hats and slickers, on the muddy ground. My brother whistles, a pretty fine imitation of a whippoorwill. After a minute, he does it again. He waits, and does it a third time. Then, he slides from the back of his horse, holding up a hand to let me know not to follow. He moves to the mouth of the cave without a sound and disappears inside.

I stay where I am. I can hear voices, but not words. Jake asking, Tommy answering. Then Jake telling, and Tommy asking. I hear Tommy's voice, sharp and angry, and Jake trying to soothe him. Tommy's voice gets more and more upset, and Jake's does, too. It's time for me to get in there.

At the mouth of the cave, I clear my throat, real loud. Both boys stop arguing and look at me. I'm nowhere near ready for what I see. Tommy has a black eye, like somebody punched him square. There's a big bruise on his jaw, and it's swollen on one side. A slash down his cheek looks almost more like a tear than a cut. I'd bet anything it was done with that broken whiskey bottle. There's another gash over the eye that ain't black. I bless whatever made me put together a medicine kit when I was rounding things up for this trip.

"This is my brother, Gus," says Jake.

"I know who he is," says Tommy. His eyes are blue, like Jake's, but Jake's have never been as cold and hard as what's looking at me now.

"Tommy, it's good that he's here," says Jake. "It'll be better this way."

Tommy shifts his glare from me to Jake. "Why's that?" I'm impressed with how he seems willing to listen to my little brother. Jake means something to him, that's clear enough.

"Because now, nobody's gonna come lookin' for you," Jake explains. "Gus is the best tracker in these parts. When he says you can't be found, ain't nobody else gonna try looking for you."

Well. If that don't beat all. That's what we call "Jake logic." If you don't look too close, it makes sense, but usually, there's at least a couple of whopping big holes in it. Like this time. First of all, a blind man could have followed Tommy's trail. What that kid doesn't know about covering his tracks would fill a box canyon.

And second, Jake's figuring I'll lie to everybody when we get back, and he should know better than that. Just when I'm about to say something like this, he shoots me a look that tells me, plain as day, to just go along for now. I cross my arms and say nothing. I figure he knows Tommy better than I do, but I hope he's got something else planned.

Tommy looks me up and down. I'd have expected the boy to be scared or skittish, but he doesn't look even a little bit nervous. Fact is, he reminds me of Pa when he's about to run somebody off the Bar J. The thought strikes me funny, since Tommy's on our land, not us on his, and I can't help smiling. Both boys look at me like I'm plumb loco.

Then I look at Tommy again, and the smile goes away. I step closer to him. "I got something in my saddlebag to clean those cuts," I say. "I'll be right back." I head back out in the rain and get my gear and Jake's. I'm back in a few minutes without ever hearing a sound from in here. When I come back, they're still standing where I left them.

I drop the gear and fish around in the saddlebags for the medicine kit. "Come here, boy," I say. I barely look up, but out of the corner of my eye, I see Jake nodding encouragement to him.

"It's okay, Gus is good at doctoring," Jake says. He should know. Sometimes, I feel like I spent half his life doctoring him. I know now that some of those times were likely when he got beat up defending Tommy.

Tommy stands there another minute. I wait without saying anything. If there's one thing I know, it's how to deal with wild critters.

This one may look like he's in charge of himself, but there's nothing to say he won't run off if we look at him wrong.

"It's okay," Jake says again. I catch his eye and shake my head a little bit, frowning. Jake gets the message and shuts up.

When nobody's said anything for a little bit, Tommy comes over to me. I tell him to sit down, but he won't, so I doctor his face standing up. The cut on his cheek is nasty and should probably get sewed up, but I didn't bring a needle and thread, so I make do with cleaning it out real good. Even though I know the arnica burns, Tommy never moves. I reckon he's felt things that hurt a whole lot worse.

"Do you have any other cuts we need to clean out?" I ask. Tommy says nothing. "Tommy, if you have other cuts and we don't do anything, you could get real sick." He looks at me, and I look at him. All of a sudden, he unbuttons his shirt and takes his left arm out of the ripped sleeve. There's another cut, almost as bad as the one on his cheek. I doctor that one and wrap a bandage around it to keep it clean. He puts his shirt back on and buttons it, all without a word. He walks back to where Jake is standing and then turns to me.

"Thank you, sir," he says, real quiet.

"You're welcome," I say, just as quiet.

Daylight's almost gone. Jake goes out to tend the horses. There's no wood around here that's dry enough to burn, but I brought a lantern with us. I measure out the oil and light the lantern. It ain't much, but it's better than pitch dark. We're here for the night, that's for sure. There's no way I'd take those two boys back down that trail at night. We're probably not more than a half a day's ride from the house, but I can't chance it.

I unroll my bedroll and set down on it to unpack the food. Daisy put up some good grub for us, sandwiches and gooseberry pie. I dole it out to the boys, giving Tommy the biggest piece of pie. The boy couldn't have had any lunch. Remembering that kitchen, I reckon he probably didn't have any breakfast, either.

"My stomach ain't feelin' right," Jake says suddenly. Before I can say anything, he goes on, "Here, you eat this. I ain't hungry." He doesn't meet my eyes as he hands his sandwich to Tommy. Tommy doesn't look like he believes Jake, but he takes the sandwich anyway.

"Jake, you gotta eat somethin'," I say. What he's trying to do is nice, but he can't go without.

"My stomach don't feel good," he insists. He sits on the bedroll next to me, and I lay a hand on his forehead. He's cool, of course.

"Maybe you'll have something later," I say. He looks up at me, and I smile the tiniest bit, just to let him know he's not fooling anybody and I'll make sure he eats before he goes to sleep. In the lantern light, I can't quite tell if he winks at me or not.

With dinner behind us, there's no more putting it off. I take a swig of water from my canteen and wish it was whiskey. "Tommy," I say. "We gotta talk about what happened today."

Even with his swollen eye, he looks at me steady and sure. "Yes, sir," he says. *Yes, sir.* The kid's got better manners than Jake. Then again, nobody beat Jake's manners into him with their fists.

I know the part Jake told me, but I need to know what happened before. I point to his face. "Did your pa do that to you?"

"Yes, sir." Truth, but no more.

I'm gonna have to drag it all out of him. "When?"

"This morning."

I need to come up with better questions. As I'm trying to think how to do it, Jake says, real simple, "Tell us what happened."

Maybe because it was Jake who asked, Tommy does. "Pa came home this morning. I don't know where he was last night. It don't matter. He was drunk when he came home. He started tearing up the house. He did that every now and again. That's why—that's why there warn't much there. Most times, he'd do that for a while, and then he'd fall down and sleep it off."

"But not this time?" I ask without thinking. Jake gives me a sharp *shut up* look.

But Tommy's not scared off. It's like he wants to tell us now. "He found the letter from my aunt," he says. "She lives in this little town just above Sacramento. Ma'd finally got up the nerve to write and ask if we could come and live with her, and she said we could. The letter came yesterday. We were gonna leave tonight after Pa went out to the saloon. She even sent money for the stage." He stops again. After a minute, he says, "Pa ain't much for readin', but he figured out what the letter was when he saw the money, and he went clean out of his mind. Hollered how she always said she'd never leave him and he'd keep her there if it was the last thing he did. She was so scared, she cried. He made my ma cry." For a second, I think I see tears in the boy's eyes, but the next instant I figure I must be wrong. His eyes are cold and hard as marbles.

"He smashed his bottle and came at her with it. She had the knife. I tried to get between them, but he shoved me out of the way. She was screaming for help, but nobody came. He jumped her, and I jumped him, but he shook me off like I was nothin'. He went at her with the bottle, and I went back after him again. Next thing I know, she was lyin' there, bleeding, and he was wiping her blood off his face. I tried to get to her, but he shoved me out of the way again. Then he came after me with the bottle—that's how I got cut up. But I got in a really good kick, and he went down." In a low voice, he said, "She was already dead, but she was still holding the knife. He started to get up, and I kicked his sorry carcass again. And then … "

Jake's sitting tight next to me, his arm pressed against mine. I can feel him trembling, and I know it's not from the cold. This is the part where he came in.

"So, you killed your pa in self-defense," I say.

Tommy looks from me to Jake. "No, sir," he says. "He was already down. And he warn't gettin' back up."

"But he attacked you," I say. "He tried to kill you. The sheriff would see that."

Tommy shakes his head. "No, sir," he says. "I ain't gonna lie. It warn't self-defense. Not the way the sheriff means." He looks me in the eye, clear and firm. If it wasn't for the bruises and cuts on his face, he'd look downright dignified. "She was already dead when I done it, and he warn't gettin' up—at least, not right then." It's almost like he wants credit for the kill.

I look at Jake. He nods. He's the one who saw the killing. If we go back, he's the one who'll have to testify against Tommy. It's his word that'll hang the boy.

I catch myself then. *If we go back.* When did there start to be a question? Jake might think we're here to help Tommy get away, but I came out here to fetch the boy and bring him back. All the way up here, it was clear as day to me: we'd take Tommy back to town and hand him over to Efraim Anderson. That's what Pa would do without a second thought. Of course, Pa'd also pay for the best lawyer in the territory to defend Tommy, but he'd never question the notion that the boy has to face up to what he did. I never questioned it, either—leastwise, not until I heard what Tommy had to say. Now, I'm not so sure.

"Tommy, what happened this morning—did this kind of thing happen a lot?" I try to be gentle with the question.

"A fair amount, sir," he says. I don't know what that means, and it must show, because he says, "Four or five times a month, maybe. It warn't as much when he was working in the mines on account of he was so tired when he got home he just fell into bed. But then he got fired for drinkin' on the job, and things got worse. The last few months, it was a couple times a week." And now, it'll never happen again, because Amos Parker is dead. Because his boy killed him.

"Why didn't you and your ma leave before this?" I ask instead.

"She wouldn't go," he says. "She said everybody always gave up on Pa, and she promised him she never would."

"But she wrote to your aunt ..."

The boy's eyes cloud over. "I wrote the letter," he says. It's the first time he sounds sorry for anything. "We'd got a letter from

Aunt Millie last Christmas. That's Ma's big sister. We hadn't heard from any of Ma's family in so long, we thought they were all dead. I guess they thought we were dead, too. But Aunt Millie wrote, and Ma wasn't gonna write back, but I told her it was our chance to get free. I wrote to Aunt Millie and told it all, and I asked if me and Ma could come and stay with her. And she wrote back and said we should come right away and she'd never tell anybody where we were. She said we could change our names and Pa would never find us." The boy swallows hard. "Ma was so scared he'd find out. At first she was gonna burn the letter, but she hid it in her bureau instead—said it was too important to burn. All day yesterday, she kept opening the drawer and touching it, like she wanted to make sure it was real. She kept saying, 'It'll all be over soon.'"

Tommy's voice fades off. He ain't crying, even though he has every right. I can feel my little brother shaking, trying not to make any noise with his own crying. I put my hand on his leg, and he holds it tight.

"But this morning—once she was dead, why didn't you just run?" I ask. I don't know why I'm asking. I don't want to hear that the boy could've gotten away scot-free, but he stayed to kill his pa anyway.

"He woulda come after me," says Tommy. "If I went to Aunt Millie, he woulda found me. I couldn't spend my whole life lookin' over my shoulder, waitin' for him to catch up with me. A man can't live like that."

A man. The boy is fourteen years old, but he's seen things I never have. I've never seen my pa come in drunk and spoiling for a fight. I never saw him lay an angry hand on my ma. When she died of the fever, he was holding her hand. He's never punched me or Jake. I've never even seen him pull a weapon on anybody who didn't draw first. But what Tommy's seen—the thought makes my stomach churn. Everything in me wants to protect him the way I try to protect Jake, but it's too late for that with Tommy. Maybe it always has been.

"Gus, he's gotta go to his aunt," says Jake. In the lantern light, I can see the tear tracks on his face. "He'll be safe there. It'll be okay."

And you won't have to testify, I think. Maybe that shouldn't matter, but it does. Tommy watches me. I can't tell what he's thinking. He doesn't say anything. Maybe he figures there's nothing left to say.

I look from one boy to the other. Two skinny kids with too-sad eyes. *Oh, sweet Lord. They're just too young for all this.* Tommy sitting there, admitting to killing his pa with no excuse the law will accept. Jake next to me, ready to do anything to keep his friend from hanging. And they're watching me like I'm supposed to know how to fix it all.

"Tommy," I say. He's on the edge of the lantern light, but I can see his eyes. A boy's eyes should never be so sad. "How long did your pa—do what he did to you?"

"As long as I can remember." It amazes me, the way he talks. No hemming or hawing. Just straight out, clear and honest, like he's got nothing left to fear.

Maybe he doesn't.

"And you're fourteen now?"

"Yes, sir."

I don't know if I'm right or wrong. Pa would say I'm wrong. He'd say no man is above the law. Except the way I see it, the law's been failing Tommy Parker his whole life. Now a good woman is dead, and the man who killed her is dead, too. I say, let the dead bury the dead, and let this boy start making himself a new life. Fourteen years of hell is enough. He's served his time.

I reach into the pocket of the vest Jake's still wearing. There's almost twenty dollars there. More than enough to get a boy to a little town just above Sacramento. I take it all out and press it into Tommy's hand.

"We're gonna go with you as far as the stage," I say. I want to use my rough voice, the one I use to make sure Jake does what he's told, but I can't. This boy's heard enough roughness to last a lifetime. "You're gonna go straight to your aunt's house, and you're gonna stay there. When you get there, you have her send me a wire so I know everything's okay."

Tommy shakes his head. "I'll have one of her neighbors send it," he says. "They'll say the package arrived." That boy is so smart. I wish he'd been smart enough to figure out how to get him and his ma away from his pa.

"If I don't get that wire in a week, I'm gonna come looking for you," I say. I try to sound gruff. "And if I do, I'll find you, just the way I did today, and I'll bring you back here to stand trial. So you better go where you're sayin', and you better stay there."

"Yes, sir." Tommy's not afraid of me. He knows what I'm saying, but he ain't upset about it. He seems to think it's fair. I reckon that, after you've seen what he's seen, there isn't much left that can upset you.

I can feel Jake's eyes on me. I don't know what we're going to tell Pa. I know Pa won't agree with me on this one, not even a little bit. Maybe I should tell Tommy not to send the wire. At least I can say I don't know where the boy is.

"Send the wire to me," Jake says suddenly. He's not looking at Tommy; he's looking at me. Without me saying a word, he knows what I'm thinking.

I shake my head firmly. "Send it to me." Jake's been keeping Tommy's secrets long enough. It's time to shift the burden off those young shoulders. He should never have had to carry it in the first place. I'll figure out what to tell Pa.

I see Jake catch Tommy's eye and shake his head slightly, and Tommy nods. Everybody's protecting everybody now. I can't help wondering where the protection was for Tommy for all these years. Wrapped up in my little brother's fists, I guess.

The only sound is the rain dripping outside. Maybe it's a trick of the lantern light, but Jake and Tommy look like men now. With all my heart, I wish they could've stayed boys just a little longer.

The walk from the livery stable to Efraim Anderson's office isn't long enough. I keep remembering how we left Tommy at the stage. The three of us rode to the way station with the morning sun at our backs. We stood around, not saying much, until we saw the stage coming. I stepped away to give Jake a chance to say his goodbyes. The stage drew to a stop, and in the noise of people talking and horses getting changed out, I took Tommy aside. "Now, you listen to me," I said, low but serious, my hand on the boy's shoulder. "You know where we are. If you have any trouble—anything—you let me know, and I'll come fetch you. I mean it. Any time at all."

For the first time since I walked into that cave, Tommy's chin trembled. His eyes glistened. Right then, he looked like a little boy. Jake nodded, laying a hand on Tommy's arm.

"You're gonna be okay now," my brother whispered, tears in his own eyes. Tommy ducked his head, and I pulled him into a hug, same as I would have done with my little brother. I heard him sniffle, and I gave him a little extra squeeze. Then I let go of him, and he stepped back, head bowed. I gave him my kerchief, and he turned away to blow his nose. When he turned back to us, he was under control.

He held out the kerchief, but I shook my head. "Thanks," he whispered. Clutching the kerchief, he climbed into the stagecoach with the other passengers. The driver slammed the door after him and they drove off, with Tommy waving out the window and us waving back until they went around a curve and disappeared from sight.

I draped my arm around Jake's shoulders as we walked back to the horses. I had no intention of taking him straight home. We needed sort things out before we had to face the sheriff and Pa. A couple of days of fishing and taking it easy, just the two of us, seemed like a good place to start.

So, we spent some time at Jake's favorite fishing place, about a half-day's ride from the house. We caught trout and cooked them over a campfire. We talked about Tommy and other stuff. I'd figured Jake might have some nightmares about what he saw at the Parkers', and he did, but I was right there, and he was fine.

We couldn't fish forever, though. There's things to be done, and one of them is talking to Efraim. That's going to be hard. I don't want to lie, but I don't know what else to do. Jake says we should just say we couldn't find him. Yep—*we*. He's coming with me. We argued halfway back to town about it. I tried to tell him he should just stay at the livery stable and curry the horses while I went to the sheriff, but he wouldn't hear of it. There's something different about that boy now, almost like he's more sure of where he stands. He's still more grass than hay, but he's not the same little brother he was just a few days ago. He's earned the right to see this through. So I tell him he can come, but he has to keep his mouth shut and let me do the talking. "We can't tell him we let Tommy go," I say.

He rolls his eyes. "You think I don't know that?"

I smack the back of his head. "Just keep your mouth shut." I'm still the big brother, even if he's catching up.

Efraim's at his desk, scribbling away about something. He looks up when we come in. He doesn't seem surprised to see it's just the two of us. "Well?" he says.

I shrug. Even though I practiced in my head what to say, I can't make it come out. "I don't know where he is," I say finally. My mouth is dry as cotton. I feel like I'm balancing on the thin edge of seven different lies, even though what I said is true: right now, at this very moment, I don't know where he is. He could be riding in the stagecoach, or sitting in a way station, or just standing beside the road, stretching his weary bones and knowing, for maybe the first time in his life, that nobody's going to come along and beat the daylights out of him.

Efraim peers at me with that way he has, like he knows everything you could possibly be keeping from him. Maybe he does. "Guess that's that, then," he says. I can't say for sure, but I think he's relieved.

After a minute, when nobody says anything else, he reaches into his desk drawer and pulls something out. A thin gold band with a tiny blue stone.

"Belonged to Mary Beth," he says. "Ida Mae found it when she was cleaning out the house." He holds it to Jake. "I reckon you know what to do with this."

He knows. "Yes, sir," says Jake, his voice barely more than a whisper. He shoves the ring in his pocket, and I fight the urge to bow my head in shame. Efraim Anderson is the most upstanding lawman I ever met. In that moment, I want to tell him I'm sorry for making him part of this. Before I can say anything, the sheriff lays a hand on my shoulder.

"Sometimes, all a man can do is what seems right at the time," he says quietly.

I don't know about that. All I know is that somewhere, there's a boy riding in a stagecoach with the wind in his face and maybe the worst part of his life finally behind him. For now, I reckon that'll have to be enough.

The Sun God Dreams of Night
by Michelle Chen

aPOLLO AMBLES THROUGH the observatory
unheeded. He tilts a telescope, gazes,

lets it glow in the ambient light
of his fingertips before recoiling,

blinded by the sunrise. You will not find this
in myth books. He made sure of it.

This is the moment he shakes
free, cuts the new fires from his toes,

alights into the shade unburdened & redacted.
The gloxinia buds bend to his muted light still.

Come dawn, when the astronomer is dozing,
Apollo hurries, lapping at the dew

that evaporates with a glance, chasing owls and
bats that flap away beyond his reach.

»

Apollo sometimes steals the stellarium key,
prays that the metal nubs will not

dissolve in his palm. Sometimes, he prays
that his tanned ankles might lose their luster.

They won't. Instead, he does what he can
to feel nocturnal—leaves his fingerprints

on penciled constellations, sneaks armfuls
of astrolabes back through the morning

to his chariot. Holds Cassiopeia to sunlight for study
like a two-headed cat or an ancient coin.

As he thumbs through, diagrams slice his hands
open and red as a sunburn. Soon, the mortals will rise.

Soon, the God of the Light must return to his
new duties—burying Helios, lending

brightness to each note of poetry, beaming
sweat across the land's epidermis,

all the while yearning for night. Until then,
he will rattle the astrolabes for their clarion call.

Pace, relentless, towards the distant dim.
Revel in the paper stars on his knees.

About the Poet

Michelle Chen is a fifteen-year-old poet, writer, and artist who lives for paper mail, warm zephyrs, and fried noodles, and who takes inspiration for her writing from the events that occur in and around her home, New York City—though her birthplace is Singapore, and she hopes to return and visit someday. She is the first-prize winner of the 2015 Knopf Poetry prize, the recipient of The Critical Junior Poet's Award, and has performed at Lincoln Center. Her work has been honored both regionally and nationally in the Scholastic Art and Writing Awards and is forthcoming in the *Sharkpack Poetry Review*, *Corium*, and *Night Train*.

The Anniversary
by Amanda Pauley

aT SOME POINT, taking a shower had become difficult, yet over the years, Maria had become accustomed to maneuvering in the limited space. She added an extra shower curtain to block off the back half of the tub, which was filled with plastic bins of rubber ducks, empty shampoo and conditioner bottles, extra washcloths, fancy soaps, and her mother's hair curlers from decades before. Now she took an efficient shower, got out, and squeezed between the three laundry bins to get to the sink. At the fogged-up mirror, she angled her body to step between piles of towels and boxes. She reached over half-full lotion bottles, old toothbrushes, and a stack of skillets balanced on the sink's edge to turn on the water and wipe the fog from the mirror.

A blurry image of her thirty-nine-year-old face emerged. Behind her, three shelves mounted on the wall were each packed to the hilt: garden tools, Swiss Army knives, a yoyo, rabbit feeders. Maria looked at her reflection. She had taken good care of her skin and avoided the sun. She walked for exercise but always used sun block. No puffiness under her eyes, something she often noticed in her elderly clients. This, her appearance, she could control for the

---

About the Author

Amanda Pauley works in McConnell Library at Radford University. She received her MFA in Creative Writing from Hollins University. Her fiction has appeared in *Shenandoah: The Washington and Lee University Review, Canyon Voices, Gravel Literary Magazine,* and many more.

time being.

After moisturizing her face, Maria followed the narrow path from the bathroom to her bedroom. Clothes were stacked in heaps on her bed and around it on the floor; the closets were full. Sometimes she could remember certain things hidden somewhere in the house. She thought about a puzzle or a table centerpiece or a keychain that she'd like to see again. She'd begin a search, but in the end the task was always too overwhelming.

She dressed and made her way back down the hall, past three large fish tanks mounted on stacks of books in the hall, each filled with half-used scented candles. She stopped to turn on the stereo, eye-level on a stack of magazines leaning against one of the fish tanks. Her home might be full and a little dusty, but it did not smell bad. She made sure of that. The thermostat was set at sixty-eight in the summer. Maria liked to think of music filling up her house while she was at work. She set the stereo to play a CD on a loop: Mozart's *Symphony No. 25 in G Minor*.

In the living room, she followed a trail walled in by antique furniture that had belonged to her great-grandmother. The surface of an oak table made in the 1800s was no longer visible, buried under the stacks of notebooks, clown figurines, and dilapidated Halloween costumes. Maria was organized about the things she needed the most: she kept one clear bin in each room, tacked to the wall at waist-high level. The one in the living room contained her car keys and her ID badge. The one in the kitchen near the back door held her purse and sunglasses. In the bin in the bedroom she kept vitamins, sleep aid medication, a photo of her mother in her younger years: a black-and-white, the tone enhancing the fair skin around dark lipstick on a hopeful smile.

It was difficult to prepare meals in the kitchen. Several toasters were stacked on top of one another and the counters were filled with jars and boxes. The toaster oven on the top leaned against the closed curtains of a small window, its blackened edges the result of a small blaze, which she had put out herself with one of the fire extinguishers she had accumulated. Usually, Maria bought a biscuit at Hardee's and ate it on the way to work, which was what she did today because today should have been a day like any other.

It wasn't, though. She drove, both hands gripping the wheel fiercely, remembering the car accident.

She walked into the Social Services building with a coffee in hand, nodded to the receptionist, and was almost through the door of her office at ten minutes to eight when her supervisor came around the hall corner.

"Oh, good. Maria, can I see you in my office as soon as you get settled?"

Maria had been on the Adult Protective Service team at Social Services for seventeen years. Her supervisors relied on her. She possessed an unusual tranquility, and she minded her own business. Her supervisors seemed to like that. Maria preferred the bottom rung and never applied for a senior worker or supervisor's position. She didn't interact much with her coworkers. She didn't dislike them, but she found socializing to be a draining effort beyond her capabilities. She tolerated team meetings and some of the in-office birthday parties and baby showers, but mostly she kept to herself. The newest director's push for bonding activities and team building exercises was exasperating.

Maria put her purse inside her desk drawer, turned on her computer, and looked around her office. Two paintings of flowers—generic tulips—hung opposite one another. Two black paper trays, very little in them, sat on her desk. One book case held orderly rows of manuals, straight and even. Other than her computer and a stack of sticky notes, nothing else was visible on the desk. Same as always, she thought. Nothing to get worked up about. Even if the anniversary feels different this year.

Maria went down the hall to her supervisor's office and knocked.

"Come on in," Jill said. "How was the weekend?"

"Fine. Is everything okay?"

"I just need to ask you a favor. You're not going to like it, but I need you to help out. I know you prefer the cases you can work on your own, but we have a new employee starting today. We've got a case that needs some attention this morning, and Darla just called in sick."

Maria's heart dropped. "Sharon's not available?"

"She's got court. Trust me, I've checked with everyone. It's been a long time since I've had to ask, and Naomi needs to get started on her training. The intake clerk should have the file on your desk by 8:30. When you're ready, take her with you."

Maria opened her mouth to say something, but she couldn't think of a good argument. Her supervisor went on to fill her in on Naomi's background. Maria was thinking about how to ward off personal questions, should Naomi be the kind of person to ask them.

Maria went back to her office to find Brenda putting the new case file on her desk.

"Good morning, Maria. Here's your case. Sounds like a hoarder."

"Another one!" Maria rolled her eyes.

"And we're taking up money for Jim's retirement party on Friday night and for a gift. Do you want to put anything in?"

Maria gave her an apologetic smile.

"I know," Brenda said. I didn't think you'd go, but I feel like I'm leaving you out if I don't ask. Have you met the new girl?"

"I'm about to. I have to take her with me today."

"They're sending her with *you*?"

Maria gave her best fake smile.

"You'll be fine. See you later," Brenda said.

Brenda was kind, Maria thought. They had worked around each other long enough to develop a comfortable, yet, office-only kind of friendship. Maria opened the file.

Naomi sat in the passenger seat of the County car, while Maria explained the case. "The neighbor said there was a bad smell coming from inside, and that she didn't look so good. She didn't let him in. She might not let us in, either. If not, we may have to involve the police, but we'll try on our own first. If she's open to a visit, we can go in and look around, make sure she's eating and is able to keep clean, and find out if she has any family or friends to help out."

Maria drove with both hands on the wheel. She had wanted to ask Naomi to drive the car, considering what day it was, but decided against it, in case it seemed strange to Naomi. Besides, this day came every year. She slowed the County car as they passed a pile of junk next to a garbage can on the curb. Maria looked at the pile.

"Some good cushions. And that dollhouse was not in real bad shape," Maria said.

"That busted up dollhouse?" Naomi asked.

Maria wanted to say how easily it might be fixed, or how its pieces could be used for something else, but she changed the subject instead. "I heard you went to Stratford. Did you do an internship somewhere?"

"I did six months at Claxton County Social Services as an aide. Mostly I made copies, did filing, and sat in on meetings. No field work."

Naomi was young and lovely. She had a readily available smile. Maria wondered what she would be like in five years, ten years. Maria had observed that people landed jobs on the Adult Protective Services team either because they were desperate for a job, or because of a desire to help people. The former came with a willingness to do anything for six months. The latter came with all of the enthusiasm in the world and a determination to change it for the better. Both either dug in and crusted over, or whimpered and left.

"Well, I'm glad you could come along today," Maria said. This wasn't true. Then again, Naomi's presence might keep her mind off of the incident twenty-three years ago—her own carelessness, the blue sky, the smell of smoke. "This may turn out to be a good example, and it helps to have another pair of eyes. She doesn't have to know that you're new. Just let me lead the conversation. You might spot something that I don't, while I'm asking questions. When we go inside, *if* we get inside, just look around. Look for safety hazards, fire hazards. Let's figure out what the smell is, and watch for signs of dementia." She had only had to take a handful of ride-alongs over the years. Some were too eager and spoke out of turn.

Others were too helpful and didn't know when to stop, to leave well enough alone. If she wasn't careful, ride-alongs could make more work for Maria than if she had gone by herself.

Edna Wilson's house was the last one on the street. It sat opposite an abandoned building that once had been Valley Foods meat processing plant but had closed ten years ago. The brick building remained vacant, windows boarded. The next-to-last house on the street belonged to a Mr. Barnes, who'd made the call on Ms. Wilson. He kept a tidy, sparse yard. Not much there, only a couple of small oak trees. Ms. Wilson's house, on the other hand, appeared consumed by vegetation. Maria and Naomi got out of the car and stood on the sidewalk in their County polo shirts, ID badges clipped just below their collars.

Several willow trees bent over the house, leaves sweeping the roof. Among the overgrown weeds and untrimmed shrubs, they could make out the remains of a garden. Four dead tomato plants were bent at the place where they were tied to their stakes, the dry brown tops touching the ground. A hoe lay on the ground next to a mound of dirt. One dried-up potato peeked out of the earth through several blackened eyes. A bucket, nearly full, sat underneath an outside spigot, a skim of greenish-brown slime covering the surface of the water.

Maria knocked at the door. They waited. Maria knocked louder. This time she heard movement from inside. The doorknob turned. They heard a lock latch, unlatch, latch, and finally unlatch again. The door opened a couple of inches, and a woman—red-eyed, wrinkled—looked out. Gray, frizzy hair formed a shape like a cap and pointed off to one side of her head. She made small movements with her head, not quite the movement of Parkinson's.

More like a nervous habit. Maria guessed her age to be a few years older than her own mother.

Maria's mother was in a nearby nursing home and often didn't appear to know Maria when she came to visit. Most of the time, they spoke like pleasant strangers, but every now and then, a recollection surfaced that Maria knew to be real. Sometimes her mother referred to the car accident as though it had just happened. Her mother's recollections surfaced in short phrases in the middle of unrelated conversation: *It was an accident, Maria dear. I was so worried when you didn't come home. Stop reading the papers.* Though the accident was the last thing in the world she ever wanted to discuss, Maria never changed the subject. The fleeting moments during which her mother recognized her were overwhelming.

"Ms. Wilson?" Maria said. "I'm Maria Parks and this is Naomi St.Clair. We're from Social Services. We received a call on your behalf and we just wanted to make sure you're okay."

"What'd they say was wrong?" Ms. Wilson asked. Through the small space of the open door, Maria could see the clutter: clothes, boxes, bottles, unidentifiable things. A mountain. Ms. Wilson wore a light green, old-fashioned dress with a large sunflower brooch pinned at the collar. Had it been clean, it would have looked nice, in a vintage post card sort of way, Maria thought. But the odor was there. Rot and excrement. From the cough behind her, Maria knew it had reached Naomi, too.

Maria sidestepped Ms. Wilson's question. "We just want to make sure you are able to get around."

"I can walk, if that's what you mean." She looked back and forth from Maria to Naomi. "Who are you with?"

"Social Services. Are you able to get outside?"

"I don't go outside much," she said. "It's so hot."

Maria did not think the air coming out of the house felt cool. If Ms. Wilson had an air conditioner, it wasn't running. "Do you have a way to get food?"

"I don't go to the store by myself, if that's what you're asking. My mother never liked to see a woman walk on the street alone."

"Could we come inside and talk to you for a minute, just to make sure you have arrangements for groceries?"

"Well, if it's just you ladies, I guess you could come in." Ms. Wilson opened the door, surprising Maria.

The smell was stronger with the door open wide. Maria heard Naomi exhale sharply, probably an in an effort not to gag. Maria concentrated on the smell, trying to decode it: Musty rooms, rotten food, and excrement, but, she was fairly certain, nothing dead. There was no sitting space and very little standing room left. The three of them stood close together just inside the front door.

A strange feeling ran through Maria, more like awe than disgust. All the lights were on, including various electric lamps on tables, on the floor, plugged in wherever possible, many with colored glass shades. A luminous circus filled the little house. The lamps lit up stacks of books, snow globes, restaurant napkins, unwashed, empty food jars with the lids screwed back on over contents growing molds in blazing greens, blues, and yellows. Stuffed animals and dolls filled one corner in a towering heap. The bottom few animals were ragged and plain, mostly Teddy Bears. Then came dolls of the Forties and Fifties. Halfway up the wall, Cabbage Patch Dolls from the Eighties. At the top of the heap, a dirty, one-armed Tickle Me Elmo smiled down at the her. In a box on a table, hundreds of pairs of eye glasses looked back and forth at each other.

In another box false teeth smiled, some uppers, some lowers, some whole sets.

"Can I get you girls something to drink?" asked Ms. Wilson.

"No, thank you. We're fine," Maria said. "Would you have somewhere we could sit down and talk for a minute? Perhaps your kitchen?"

"Well, you could come in the kitchen, but I have to warn you," she paused for a minute-long coughing spell; Maria and Naomi exchanged looks. "It's kind of a mess."

Ms. Wilson started down the hall. Maria stood still a moment longer looking at a fish tank full of hundreds of half-used bottles of nail polish. The colors shimmered in the light, despite the smudged, dirty glass of the tank.

The hallway was lined with piles. Stacks footed with newspapers, gloves and coats, then topped with layers of everything: screwdrivers and books and clothes, empty folders and broken electronics. Some of the stacks made it half way up the wall and leaned on one another for support. One bedroom door stood open. As they went by, Maria looked into a room filled with a sea of floating jars, plastic jugs, and parts of furniture. A small path led to a pile of blankets on the floor. The imprint of a head on the little pillow was still there. The corner of a mattress angled upward out of the chaos. It provided a kind of shelf, though slightly tilted, big enough for a full coffeemaker sitting at a slant, and plugged in somewhere, its tail of a cord disappearing into the sea of things. The door to the bathroom stood wide open, the toilet filled almost to the brim with excrement. At the end of the hallway, the three passed a closed door before going into the kitchen.

The kitchen table was piled with plastic trays. Fuzzy cantaloupe rinds filled a bin, brown banana peelings filled another. Material and sewing scraps filled several more. Maria breathed through her mouth. When Ms. Wilson turned away, Maria looked at Naomi and pointed toward her own mouth and motioned for her to breathe that way. Naomi nodded, but she looked pale.

"Here. One of you could sit on this crate," Ms. Wilson said, and before either Maria or Naomi could say anything, Ms. Wilson overturned a small plastic crate of magazines, emptied it onto the floor, and then made a seat. Ms. Wilson and Maria sat down at the table. Naomi took the crate.

"So, what brings you here?" Ms. Wilson asked. She made small deliberate movements with her hand, sometimes tapping on the table softly, sometimes rubbing her hands together.

"A neighbor is worried about you," Maria explained again.

"Oh, I bet you spoke to Mr. Barnes. He's a nice neighbor, though my husband never did care for him." She picked up some grey felt from a box under the table and ran her fingers over the smoothness. "Couldn't you make something lovely out of this?" She held the piece up to Naomi. "I had a dress of this material." She smiled at them with watery eyes.

"You sure could," Naomi answered. "It's beautiful."

"Your husband?" This was news to Maria.

"He and Mr. Barnes used to get into it over the fence outside. Ernest, my husband, thought Mr. Barnes was moving the fence over into our yard little by little, taking up more of our space. He was sure our yard was getting smaller."

Maria wondered how long ago Ms. Wilson's husband had passed.

"Does anyone else live with you now?" Maria asked.

"Just my husband. Ernest has trouble sleeping, so he sleeps in that bedroom there." She pointed to the closed door in the hallway.

Under the table, Maria twisted the ring around her on her finger. Had she misunderstood? Naomi looked at her in a way that confirmed she hadn't.

"Is …" Maria hesitated. Mr. Barnes hadn't mentioned a husband. "Is your husband home?"

"He is. He's sleeping. Do you want me to get him up?"

"No, you don't have to do that. We can talk to you for now. I just don't want him to be alarmed to see us here if he wakes up."

"Oh, he doesn't mind company." Ms. Wilson continued to sort through plastic spoons and fabric on the table. She put some felt pieces in an envelope. She stopped moving her hands for a moment and grimaced. On her elbow was a large blue-black bruise.

"My arm is sore," she said. I think I fell."

"It looks painful," Maria said. "We should let a doctor look at that."

Ms. Wilson looked at the two of them and was quiet for a minute. "Are you ladies from the church down the street?"

"No, ma'am. We're from Social Services. We're here to make sure you're doing okay and have food to eat. Just to see if you need someone to help you out. Did you attend the church down the street?"

"Which church?" Ms. Wilson asked.

"The one you mentioned. Just down the street." Had they passed a church? Maria couldn't remember.

"St. Andrews is just down the street," Naomi offered.

"I don't know about any church. I haven't been in years." Ms. Wilson said.

"Would you let us take you to the doctor to get your arm looked at?" Maria pointed toward the bruise. "It may need some attention."

"Oh no, I can't go to the doctor. They would charge me an arm and a leg. I'm sure it will heal soon."

"How long ago did you fall?"

Ms. Wilson looked at the felt scraps. Maria wondered if Ms. Wilson had heard her, or if she couldn't remember the fall, and when it had occurred. She sensed she'd asked a question Ms. Wilson simply couldn't answer. She decided to change the subject. She had noticed a small bowl on the floor under the table.

"Do you have any pets?" she asked.

"I used to. Smokey, a little grey fluffy thing. He was so sweet. Until he got hungry, then he would bite at my ankles. When he passed, it broke my heart. I couldn't stand the thought of getting another in his place. I still miss him."

"We're sorry," said Naomi, "It's hard to lose a pet."

"Ms. Wilson, did you have breakfast this morning?" Maria asked.

"I don't usually eat breakfast. I just have coffee and then an early lunch."

"Okay. Do you have enough food for the week?"

"Well, I think so."

"So, your husband can still go to get groceries?"

"Oh no, my husband passed away almost ten years ago."

At that, Maria looked at Naomi. Naomi's eyes were focused on the floor in the hallway. Maria turned slowly to the hall and saw nothing, but she jumped when something brushed her ankle. A tiny gray Persian cat curled around the legs of the chairs. It didn't look emaciated, but it was hard to tell on a Persian with so much hair. It hopped onto Maria's lap and then up onto the table where it barely had room to stand between the bins.

"There you are, Smokey," Ms. Wilson reached out to pet the cat. "Let me get Smokey something to eat." Ms. Wilson got up and opened the refrigerator. The rot inside was gut-wrenching. Things grew from open bowls and clung to one another or the inside of the refrigerator.

Naomi stood up. "I need to go outside," she said quietly.

Maria watched Ms. Wilson's put green slices of something— meat? — in a bowl for Smokey. Smokey wolfed it down.

"Ms. Wilson, I don't think your refrigerator is working right. We may need to get that fixed. Do you have any family?"

"I have a sister, but she hasn't been by in a while. She's upset with me. We argue. She's always trying to get me to get rid of my stuff. She complains about it being messy in here, but I don't have anything I want to get rid of."

"I'm sorry to hear that. Do you think I could call her to see if she could come and help you out again?" Maria asked. Naomi returned and sat back down on the bucket. Maria thought she looked a little red-eyed. She'd probably vomited.

"Well, I guess you could try, but I don't think she'll come."

"Do you have her phone number written down somewhere?"

"I do," she said. "Let me go check my bedroom."

Ms. Wilson left the kitchen. Maria whispered, "Are you okay?"

Naomi nodded and reached down to pet Smokey.

Maria thought Naomi looked childlike stroking the cat. She began to regret that this was her first encounter in the field, though it certainly could have been worse. Maria hoped Naomi's next experience would be less dismal. For now, she would make every effort to show Naomi ways that they could help Ms. Wilson.

Ms. Wilson came back with a small notebook. She looked through the book and came to a name and pointed. Maria wrote it down.

"I'll give her a call and see if she can help us out. Ms. Wilson, I don't see a smoke detector in your kitchen anywhere. If you don't mind, I'd like to make sure you have working smoke detectors in your other rooms. You have quite a bit of stuff that looks flammable. If you don't have any, we can get some for you for free. Would you mind if we checked to make sure your smoke detectors work?"

"Well, we can look, I guess. Are you here about the plumbing?"

"No, ma'am. We're from Social Services, but we're going to see about getting your toilet fixed, too, if that's okay with you. Let's start with the smoke detectors. May I look in the other rooms?"

"Have I had a fire?"

"No, ma'am. But we want to make sure you don't. We're going to check for smoke detectors, okay?"

"Okay."

Maria let Ms. Wilson go first into the hall. Naomi followed.

Ms. Wilson stopped at the closed door. "This is where my husband used to sleep."

Maria held her breath. Ms. Wilson pushed the door open.

The room was full of death, but no dead man in sight. Old plants were everywhere, dry and brown, in old caked dirt in pots large and small. The pots were stacked to the ceiling. Magazines filled some of them. There was just enough room for Maria to step in and look around. No smoke detector, but plenty more newspapers stacked on the bed. Maria looked at the headlines. They were from the fifties: *Brinks Robbery in Boston; Almost 3 Million Stolen*, and *Julius and Ethel Rosenberg sentenced to death for passing atomic secrets to Russians*, and *Martin Luther King, Jr. leads black boycott of Montgomery, Ala., bus system.*

"None in here," she said to Naomi. "Let's check the living room."

Ms. Wilson went with them from room to room while Maria made a list of things that would need to be taken care of. Back in the kitchen, Maria was able to move enough of Ms. Wilson's things to see the wall behind the refrigerator. She was relieved at one easy fix: the refrigerator's electric cord had only been dislodged. Maria plugged it back in. It whirred and choked to life while she explained to Ms. Wilson that they would be back with food, and some smoke detectors. Maria thought that, and cleaning out the refrigerator, would be enough to start with. The next step would be convincing her to see a doctor, getting the coffee pot moved to the kitchen, and figuring out if she had any money to buy food or if she would need a food stamp application.

Naomi was quiet on the drive back to the office.

"You okay?" Maria asked.

"Yeah. I just . . ."

Maria nodded. "The smell?"

"No, it was the husband. Thinking he's in the other room, when he's really dead. How long before she thinks he's around somewhere again? What a sad way to be. I didn't want her to see me cry."

"I know. It's awful. You did great, by the way. Even if you had to cry. Shows you've got a heart. And the fact that you kept your

breakfast down means you've got an iron stomach. We may be able to help her, depending on what we find out about her relatives." She paused. "Things will get to you from time to time, you know."

"What do you do? To cope?" Naomi asked.

Maria cleared her throat. She looked in the rearview mirror at her own face, then looked ahead and readjusted her hands on the steering wheel. "Oh, I've got my hobbies. And I like music. Classical music. Meditation. Traveling." She felt her voice trail off.

Back at the office, Maria showed Naomi how to sign the car back in. A supervisor reclaimed Naomi in order to fill out new hire forms, promising to return her to Maria after lunch.

Maria went across the street and picked up her usual turkey sandwich from Subway. Back in her office, she shut the door and ate slowly, leafing through a travel magazine she kept in her desk. Then she wiped her desk clean and got to work.

By the time Naomi joined her, she had made some progress. Ms. Wilson had been right the second time. According to the neighbor, her husband had passed away ten years ago. Mr. Barnes had helped her out until about three years ago, when the dementia set in and she wouldn't let him in the door sometimes, because she thought her husband was still alive and that he wouldn't like Mr. Barnes coming, and sometimes because she just didn't recognize Mr. Barnes. Ms. Wilson's sister had died three weeks ago, according to an obituary in the local paper from around the date that Mr. Barnes said Ms. Wilson had quit coming out of the house. According to the obit, her sister had a daughter living in California. If Maria could get Ms. Wilson to sign a Consent to Exchange Information, she could try to contact the daughter for help. The daughter might be able to help them figure out if Ms. Wilson has enough money for her daily needs.

"That may take some time, so either way, we need to go ahead and petition the court for an ECO," Maria explained to Naomi.

Naomi sat across from Maria in the bare office. "An ECO?"

"An Emergency Custody Order," Maria said. "For someone with that degree of dementia, she's obviously not able to provide for herself. If it were just a matter of getting food to her we could work with that, but that arm looked bad. If we get an ECO, there will probably be an administrative hearing at the hospital where they'll determine if medical or psychological evaluations are needed. They may end up detaining her. We've got an emergency fund for our team that we can pull from to use to buy food for her today. We'll see if she'll let us remove some of that stuff out of the kitchen.

I'll ask her again if she'll go to the doctor for her arm. If she won't, then we'll have to wait on the ECO and get her in there for everything at once. So, if you want to sit down at my computer, I'll walk you through the forms and documentation to get things started and then we'll get some fresh food to her before the day is over."

They switched seats. Maria watched Naomi adjust the chair. How young she looked. Maria tried to remember herself before the accident, not so much how she had looked, but how she had felt. She couldn't. She couldn't locate anything beyond her current state. The work-to-get-through-each-day-and-if-you're-lucky-you'll-end-up-helping-someone-else feeling.

After the computer work was done and some letters were mailed out, Maria and Naomi signed out a car and left the office again.

"We'll swing by Kroger and get food supplies," Maria said, "but I want to stop by my house first. I've got one of those raised toilet seats with handles that my mother used after surgery. I noticed Ms. Wilson had trouble getting up and down. Once we clean that toilet out, we'll stick that on there." Maria said.

At her house, she parked in the driveway and turned off the engine. "I'll be right back."

She went around back, having ceased using the front door years ago. She went inside, followed the narrow path to the bedroom, and tried to remember where she had packed away the toilet seat. Minutes ticked by as she surveyed her stuff. She checked the bathroom, and then remembered the hall closet, which she hadn't opened in years. She pulled on the door, but it was stuck. She pulled harder. She gave it one last yank with everything she had, and the closet door burst open.

The volume of its contents took Maria to the floor. A stuffed zebra, leg warmers, a wooden spatula, a tennis racquet, Tupperware containers, books, shoeboxes, marbles, a flyswatter, paper bags, curtains, a lampshade.

She heard a sharp *Oh!* and looked up to see Naomi standing in the doorway, eyes wide. Naomi was not looking at her, but at the kitchen and down the hall, at the floors and the shelves.

Twenty-three years ago, Maria had looked up from the ground to see a stranger surveying the wreckage on the road with a different wide-eyed expression. Maria had been on the pavement of the highway then, after the accident. She had been adjusting the radio—so she could hear Madonna's *Like a Virgin*—and had drifted over the edge of the shoulder. When she overcorrected, she hit a Buick in the passing lane. The truck behind Maria didn't have time to stop, and Maria's Chevy had ended upside down on the highway. Maria had undone her seatbelt and climbed out the window. Someone from another vehicle got out to find Maria bruised but alive.

"Are you okay? Can I help you up?" Naomi asked.

Maria put her hand up abruptly. "I'm fine." She knew her tone was curt.

"I just came to ask if I could use your bathroom," Naomi said.

"Oh. It's that way," Maria pointed. "I have to warn you. It's kind of a mess."

Naomi went in the direction she pointed. Maria felt enormous irritation. She would have to re-stuff the closet. And it would have to wait until she got home, when she knew she'd be tired. She was frustrated with Naomi for coming in unannounced. Still on the floor, she looked at her watch. She *had* been inside a while. She couldn't blame Naomi for coming in to check on her or to use her bathroom. It tugged at her though, what she had said to Naomi just now: *I have to warn you, it's kind of a mess.*

But this was different, she thought. Just then, she saw the end of the toilet seat sticking up out of the pile of what remained in the closet.

Back in the car, Maria and Naomi rode in silence. Maria knew what Naomi was thinking. Well, it wasn't the same, she thought. It wasn't the same at all.

On the way into Ms. Wilson's with the groceries, they met Mr. Barnes in his yard, who thanked them for their help. Inside, Ms. Wilson mentioned her husband's passing, and then the cat's passing, as well. Maria nodded to Naomi to explain that her cat was not dead, and that she needed to keep feeding it. Maria had sprung for cat food out of her own pocket, since the APS fund did not allow for pet food. While Naomi reminded Ms. Wilson of the cat's existence, Maria picked out a small plate, cleaned it as best she could, put some cat food on it and placed it where she thought the cat could find it. Then Maria put on latex gloves and with a trowel and a bucket from Ms. Wilson's yard, began to remove enough of the excrement from the broken toilet, so that Ms. Wilson could continue to use it until the plumber came in the morning. While Ms. Wilson waited in the kitchen, Naomi brought in more supplies from the car.

In the bathroom, Maria was on her hands and knees.

Naomi came to the door. "Maria," she said.

Maria looked up at her. There was pity in Naomi's eyes, but there was something else, too. She was clearly taking in what she was seeing in this moment, this foul bathroom and Maria on her knees, working up a sweat. She could tell Naomi was deciding something right then. She could feel it.

"I think," Naomi said finally, "that from the looks of things, we'll need a litter box for Smokey, too."

"Good thought." Maria went back to scooping. "We can fix a temporary one up with a box of dirt before we go."

Smokey did not make a second appearance.

Maria was exhausted that evening when she pulled into her driveway and walked up the walk in a yard that looked like all of the other yards in the neighborhood. Inside, she put her pocketbook and badge in the bin in the kitchen. Then she got a cup of water and went down the pathway toward her recliner, where she planned on sleeping that evening. She had to climb over the pile of things that had exploded from the hall closet earlier. She'd pack that back in another day.

My cups are clean.

She drank, put her head back, and listened to the music still playing.

My house doesn't smell.

A day never went by without the memory of the burning Buick, the lady she had killed. Accident. Everyone had used the word accident, except for the judge. Involuntary manslaughter was the term in the courtroom. Thanks to her age—she had been sixteen—and an expensive lawyer on which her mother spent her savings, Maria had been sentenced only to probation.

Greta, the lady in the Buick, had been thirty-nine years old. She'd had two children at home, one twelve, and the other thirteen. It had been 1985, the year the Challenger exploded. Ronald Regan was in his second term. The deterioration of the ozone layer was in the news. People were afraid of AIDS. As far as Maria was concerned, the world had stopped that summer day. With nothing more than bruises, cuts, and scrapes, she had returned home from the hospital to read the story in the paper about the dead woman.

She had turned down a scholarship to Georgetown. She attended the local university and then took the job at Social Services. She stayed in the house she'd grown up in. Ten years ago, Alzheimer's had landed her mother in the nursing home.

At first Maria had begun keeping things that made her happy: children's toys, pictures of baby animals, thousand-piece puzzles of castles and exotic landscapes. Then she just kept things.

This year Maria was the age that Greta had been when she died. Maria had had to forgive herself many times over in the past, but from here on out, she knew that every day of her life was one more day than Greta got.

Maria moved the lever and lay back in the recliner. What would Greta have thought, had she known that Tuesday morning, that her life was to be ended in an instant by a young girl?

She closed her eyes and listened to the violins and cellos in the music that had played since morning. The horns and trumpets, lovely and triumphant. The tempo moved from largo to allegro. A crescendo was balanced by a diminuendo. Then somewhere among the clarinets and oboes there was a new sound. A percussion far different from the timpani of Mozart's style. More wooden, like someone knocking on her back door.

Spitting Image
by George Wells

D ANIELLE STOOD ON the edge of the walk. She had checked the address three times now, but was still unsure. What if she had come to the wrong house, the wrong Carol Hunter?

In for a penny, in for a pound, as her English teacher was fond of saying.

She folded the paper and stuffed it in her back pocket, took a deep breath and marched to the front door, but once there, her finger hovered over the button for a few seconds as she considered turning and going home. There was still time. She could go home before her parents started to worry. She pushed the doubt away and pressed. A long buzz came from behind the door as she leaned into the plastic disc.

"I'm coming. Just a moment."

Only then did Danielle realize that she hadn't stopped pressing. She whipped her hand to her side, poised to run, but told herself to stand firm.

In for a penny …

The door opened and a woman poked her nose between the bars

ABOUT THE AUTHOR

George Wells lives in Guadalajara, Mexico, where he teaches English as a Foreign Language and writes. He is a regular contributor to *Spark: A Creative Anthology*, where he also fills the role of Writer Liaison; his work has appeared in *Shadow Road Quarterly* and *Pidgeonholes*; and he is the managing editor of *Zetetic: A Record of Unusual Inquiry.*

of the outer door. "Yes?"

Danielle froze at the sight of her own face—older, and with a smaller nose, but unmistakable all the same. She thought of *The Picture of Dorian Gray* and suppressed a laugh she knew wouldn't be appropriate.

The woman repeated, "Yes? Can I help you?"

"I … um … you …"

The woman grabbed the bars next to her face. "Listen, girl. I'm kind of busy, so whatever it is, I ain't buying. Thanks, but no thanks."

"It's not that. I'm not selling anything."

"The Good Word, then? I already heard it. Didn't do me no good." She backed into the house and started to close the door.

Danielle blurted, "Danielle! I'm Danielle, I mean. That's me."

Closing the door, the woman shot back, "I don't know any Danielle. Sorry."

"Carol? Carol Hunter?"

The door stopped before latching and swung open. "I told you—"

The woman looked Danielle over. "Oh. I guess I do know who you are." She unlatched and opened the outer door, waving Danielle into the house after her. "I'm sorry, the house is kind of a …" She steadied herself on the back of a couch covered with a threadbare sheet with a faded blue flower print, blocking Danielle's entry through the narrow entryway. "What are you doing here? You weren't supposed to … it was a closed adoption."

Danielle reached a hand out to comfort her, but decided against it and pulled her hair behind her ear instead. "I found some papers in my parents' stuff, and got on the Internet, and these days—"

"These days you can do it all with the Internet, yeah." She let go of the couch and stood straight, wringing her hands. She nodded towards the kitchen and walked to the table. "Can I get you something ... Danielle, is it?"

"Danielle."

"Danielle. Okay." She turned to face the girl. "Wow. You look just like him."

"Him? My father? I was thinking that I look like you."

"Me? No. Well, maybe a little, yeah. The shape of your face, a bit around the mouth, but you're the spitting image of him." She blew through tight lips and puffed cheeks and stepped to the refrigerator. "Can I get you something, Danielle? A soda? I'll be having a beer, myself, if you don't mind."

Danielle sat in an office chair at the head of the table. "A Coke, please, if you have it."

Carol gave Danielle the drink in a can and popped open her beer as she sat down in a wicker chair. "Sorry about the décor. Jim calls it 'eclectic', which is his cute way of saying 'take whatever leftovers you can get for cheap or free.'"

Danielle spun the can on the table without opening it. "That's okay. It's interesting."

"That it is, Danielle." She sipped her beer. "So, what ... what can I do for you, Danielle?"

Danielle snapped her head up. "Do? Nothing. I mean I just wanted to meet you. Meet my mother."

"Don't you already have a mother?" Carol put one hand to her chest, touched Danielle's arm with the other. "Oh, no. Did something happen to her?"

"No, no, no, nothing like that. She's fine. My parents are fine, and they're great, but ... "

"But what, sweetie?"

"I wanted to meet my real mother."

She pulled her hand back. "Oh, Danielle. You have a real mother, and I'm not her."

Danielle opened her Coke. "I know, I didn't mean that, I was just curious."

"About what, Danielle?"

"About you, about my father."

"I don't know what to tell you."

Danielle took a drink of her Coke, set it down, and stared at the line of liquid stuck in the rim. "Why … ?" She raised her eyes, but not her head.

"Oh, honey. I was young and poor and not very happy. Unhappy women don't raise happy children. I knew I would never be able to give you what you needed. Gabe—that was his name—he was gone soon as the stick changed color, and I didn't have two nickels to rub together. I didn't like the other option, so …"

Danielle crossed her arms across her chest, silent tears running down her cheeks. "So just like that, you give me away?"

"'Just like that?' Listen, girl, until you walked in somebody's shoes, don't go judging. It wasn't at all easy, but it was right, and I got no regrets here. Fifteen years later and I still don't have nothing to offer you but a soda and a sob story. And I'm about to give you the door. You weren't supposed to come, anyways."

Danielle dropped her head and wiped her face.

Carol rubbed the girl's shoulder. "Oh, shoot. I'm sorry, honey. It's just … you know … maybe you can tell me about your parents."

"What about them?"

"What are they like? I never met them."

Danielle wiped her nose on her sleeve. "They're insurance brokers."

"Both of them?"

"Yeah, they met on the job, but Dad got a transfer after they started dating."

Danielle told Carol about herself, her childhood in a middle class neighborhood, her friends at school, her aspirations to a career in nursing. "I know that seems girly, like girls today should want to be doctors, but I think nurses do a lot of good."

Carol gave Danielle an overview of her life, her economic struggles. She started as a waitress, eventually becoming manager of a small diner. Her husband was a mechanic. The money wasn't bad, but a series of health problems kept them on this side of comfort. They never had children. "Jim can't. I'm as fertile as they come, but he's got slow swimmers." She said they were happy, though.

After an hour, Danielle told her that she had to get home. "My parents will be worrying about me."

As they said their goodbyes at the door, Carol told her, "Thank you for visiting, Danielle, but ... "

"I shouldn't come back."

Carol nodded. "I think it would be best."

"Okay. Can I ask you something? Did you ever … ?"

"Think about you? Yeah, all the time. Now I know. So do you." She gave her an awkward hug. "Thank you."

"Mom, I'm home."

"There you are. Where were you?" Her mother rushed to the front door. "We've been calling and calling."

"Sorry. My phone ran out of juice. I was at the mall and lost track of time. Dinner smells good."

"Lasagna. Wash up and we'll eat."

She washed her hands in the kitchen sink, and her father sat at the head of the table in the dining room. She dried her hands on a kitchen towel. "Guys?"

Her mother cut into the lasagna as her father draped his napkin in his lap. "What's up?" he asked.

"Who do you think I take after more—you, or Mom?"

Seven

by Sophia Diggs-Galligan

I N THESE sunlit last
moments,
you might have formed one
last word on broken lips,
from a broken mind,
halved,
pithed,
diced,
doused in iodine antiseptic
sold by the ounce.

but I saw no spark in your
unwavering open eyes,
and no whisper or sharp cry of one
last word,
(cueing the instrumentalists, who
weep into their violas)
echoed in these hospice
hallways.

»

ABOUT THE POET

Sophia Diggs-Galligan is from Washington, D.C., and is inspired to write by everything: nature, books, and random strangers; by her family, friends, and wonderful writing teacher. She is the recipient of the Larry Neal Award for poetry and a Gold Medal in poetry in the Scholastic Art and Writing Awards.

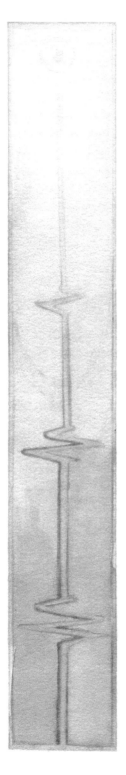

It would have been perfect—
punctuating
this silenced
decade of your life,
ironic,
sweet,
with close-ups of both of our roman noses,
silhouetted by
fluorescent bulbs,
and white noise,
you would be
silent again for the last
time,
and just as the
music crescendoed,
you would shut your
eyes, and I would
rest assured that you had
lived the right life and died
the right death,
and our performance would be given 5 stars
by the LA Times.

But you didn't, instead staying
silent
until the end,
where the only sound was the incessant
bleeeeeeeeeeeeeeeeeep
of the heart monitor,
leaving me no
movie cameras to continue the
struggle for.

For the life of me,
I can't remember
what your last words were because
I always assumed
there would be more.

Fallen Angels
by John Biggs

"IT'S A BAD LUCK sky." Lizbeth's mom pointed a finger at the first shooting star of the evening. She made the sign of the cross—Catholic style, even though she was a Baptist.

"Stars cast out of heaven like fallen angles. Bad times are on the way."

Mom said the same thing every August when the meteor shower came. Sometimes she was right, like when the Germans invaded Poland. Sometimes she was wrong, like when the family cow gave birth to twin calves. Sometimes she was half-way-wrong, like when the neighbor boy, Tommy Hotabee, came back from the war last fall—crippled but still alive.

Lizbeth helped her dad carry wooden lawn chairs from their front porch into the yard. She lined them in a row like the seats in the Orpheum Theater in Idabel. Four pine chairs painted white so they stood out like ghosts. One for mom, one for dad, one for Lizzy, and one for Tommy, who looked like he'd fall over if he didn't sit down pretty soon.

"Stars falling into the woods are bound to stir up crooked spir-

---

ABOUT THE AUTHOR

John T. Biggs is an award-winning author with sixty short stories published in magazines and anthologies that range from literary to young adult and everything in between. Most of his work, including "Fallen Angels," has strong Native American content. John has published two novels—*Owl Dreams* and *Popsicle Styx*—with Pen-L Publishing, and a collection of linked short stories titled *Sacred Alarm Clock* released by Oghma Creative Media.

its." Mom knew the meteors weren't really stars. She knew most of them never hit the ground, but she was an old-time Choctaw, and old-time Choctaw talked that way.

"Real bad luck," she said. "Bad luck anyone with eyes can see."

Lizbeth and Tommy sat in the two middle chairs. Mom and dad sat on the outside like a pair of mismatched bookends. It was a perfect meteor shower night. The crescent moon was a sliver, no clouds in the sky and a new spark streaked by every minute. Sometimes they came in twos and threes.

Pretty, is what Lizbeth thought. Better than talking pictures. Better than radio. Better than Fourth of July parades in McAlester.

"The spirits give fair warning." Mom pointed her voice right at Tommy Hotabee, as if maybe he would listen to her stories.

"Always bad luck for somebody." She nodded at Tommy's crippled leg as if that proved her point.

Tommy kept his eyes on the sky, flinched when a shooting star flew by. Every now and then his hands would stray to his injured leg. Rub the place where the bullet struck him.

Lizbeth wanted to tell him that bad luck bullet had nothing to do with meteors. She invited Tommy over to listen to the president—Roosevelt—on the radio. Thought it would cheer him up to find out how the war was going now that he was back home, but Tommy didn't look cheerful. Mom's talk of bad luck and evil spirits wasn't helping and it didn't look like she'd stop anytime soon. She told Tommy how the Choctaw had been watching everything that happened since the world was made. They made a list of bad luck things. Owls, and shooting stars. Coyotes were the worst.

"Our people know these things. Mark my words."

She had more to say but dad told her to, "Hush." He bobbed his head toward Tommy Hotabee who'd curled up in his chair like he was freezing cold.

"You'll scare your daughter." Dad winked at Lizbeth so she'd know it was the Hotabee boy he was really worried about.

Tommy stared at the shooting stars and rocked back and forth hard enough to make his chair squeak. He had two good legs when they sent him across the ocean to fight the Germans. He had one when they sent him home.

Lizbeth thought he had a lot worse injuries than a shot-up leg. Injuries that didn't leave scars where they would show.

"It's the Perseid meteor shower." Dad moved the conversation from Choctaw spirits to astronomy just like that. He pronounced the scientific words as slow and clear as a college professor. He walked over to Tommy and put a hand on his shoulder.

Dad read the Farmer's Almanc. Knew all about the stars and the planets and the little specks of dust that seemed to fly out of the Perseus constellation every summer.

"Don't hurt nobody," he said.

Tommy uncurled for a second. "Those meteors look like tracer bullets." He rubbed the place on his leg where a German soldier shot him and stared at the bright specks of bad luck dust blowing like campfire sparks across the sky.

Lizbeth asked him, "What's a tracer bullet?" This week, President Roosevelt's broadcast was all about the war. He never mentioned bullets—not even once. Lizbeth couldn't remember that he ever did.

"Tipped in phosphorous," Tommy told her. "Leave streaks behind them where they burn the air."

Dad pointed to an extra bright shooting star. Said those meteors were specks of dust were left over from where a comet passed. "Like Halley's comet."

Dad told how Halley's comet came the year Mark Twain was born, and how it came again the year he died.

Dad said comets travel in circles. They come around again and again, but usually it takes so long one person doesn't live long enough to see the same one twice.

"Orbits," Dad said, "are the circles comets move in."

Mom thought comets were bad luck too.

"Warnings," she said. "For those smart enough to listen."

"Tracer bullets," Tommy said, "don't warn you until the shooting's already started." The government sent him home after he was shot, but the war followed him every limping step he took.

"You can smell the burnt phosphorous when they come close." He sniffed the air, checking to see if the shooting stars gave off a scent. "Tracers burn when they hit you."

He said the burning never stopped once it took hold. "Even on the coldest day. "Even if you cover it in ice."

Lizbeth walked over to Tommy's chair and put her hand on his wounded leg.

"It's hot," she said. The scar felt like a knotted piece of rope underneath her fingers, feverish to the touch. The muscles moved like worms inside the skin but after a while they settled down. Tommy's leg relaxed and cooled; the wrinkles in his forehead went smooth.

Mom was about to tell Lizbeth it wasn't lady like for a girl to touch a wounded soldier on the leg. "Thirteen years old is …"

But Tommy interrupted before she had a chance to finish. "You've got the healing touch, Lizzy. Better than the medics. Better than the nurses in the VA Hospital."

It was the first time anybody had seen Tommy Hotabee smile since he came back from the war. He lay back in his wooden chair and looked the Perseid meteors like they were something pretty instead of something dangerous.

"Look there." He pointed to a cloud of bats jittering across the crescent moon.

"More bad luck for sure," Mom said. "Shooting stars, then bats."

The bats wings reflected the moonlight like leaves on a silver maple tree fluttering in the wind before a storm. Kept everybody's eyes turned to the sky because it looked like mom was right about messages from the spirits.

A meteor streaked across the sky between the moon and the bats. Another followed and then two more, close together so all four were in the sky at once, four bright lines underneath the moon. Then a bigger spark shot across the sky. Bright red, like a horseshoe heated in a blacksmith's forge. Noise followed this one. A heavy rolling sound like a train loaded with crooked spirits. The red spark burst over our heads like a roman candle. The smaller bits were soaked up in the darkness, but the biggest piece crashed into the Kiamichi Mountains. A flash and a puff of smoke—a rumbling noise came afterward.

"Artillery!" Tommy curled up in his chair again waiting for more bombs to fall.

"That was close." Lizbeth's heart raced, the way it did when she ran home from school. For a few seconds she couldn't tell if she felt fear or excitement.

"I want to go find it." She decided on excitement. "I've got to go find it."

They watched a streamer of smoke drift up from the mountains.

A mile away, more or less. On a straight line between the back of their house and a jagged mountaintop shaped like a broken nose.

"Looks easy to find, but it probably ain't." Lizbeth's dad was the expert on falling stars. He looked excited, too. "Look for it tomorrow, Lizzy. Right now, you need to walk Tommy back to his house."

"I guess it's pretty late." Tommy stumbled a little when he stood up. Hopped on his good leg for a few seconds before he trusted his weight on the bad one. Lizbeth steadied him with an arm around his waist.

"Thanks, Lizzy." Tommy looked past the tomato garden through the thin strip of windbreak trees that separated his house from Lizbeth's. Like he was looking for German snipers or maybe Choctaw spirits.

//

"Don't go too far." Mom stood beside Lizbeth in the shadow of their house and watched the Kiamichi mountains change color in the light from rising sun. "It's easy for a girl your age to go too far. Not so easy to find your way back home."

"If I can't find it by noon, I'll turn around." Lizbeth looked at to the rolling hills southwest of her house still shrouded in morning mist. No sign of where the meteor struck—like it was one of Mom's imaginary spirits that disappeared with the first light of morning.

"Mountains are bigger than they look from far away." Mom handed Lizzy a lunch wrapped in brown butcher paper: homemade bread, smoked ham, and a Mason jar filled with well water.

"Empty stomachs make for bad decisions, Lizbeth." She got the far away look in her eyes that came before stories about spirits who feasted on souls and witches who turned into owls.

"Be careful." That was what everything came to in the end. "If something doesn't feel right, don't do it." She kissed Lizbeth on the forehead and turned to look at the morning sun. It's lower edge had cleared the trees in the eastern forest that ran across the Winding Stair mountains that straddled the Oklahoma-Arkansas border.

"It'll turn dark faster than you expect."

Lizbeth walked away before her mom could change her mind. She didn't look back at her house until her mother was a tiny silhouette backlit by the rising sun. When she was too far away to hear if mom called her back, Lizbeth turned and waved. Then she stepped into the hardwood forest at the edge of the Kiamichi mountains.

More hills than mountains, really. Nothing like the famous mountains Lizbeth read about in school. Nothing like the Himalayas that rise so high there's not enough air at the top to breath, or the Rocky Mountains—the ones her people called the Backbone of the World—or the Alps, where a German soldier fired a bullet that crippled Tommy Hotabee.

But according to Mom, there were Choctaw spirits hiding in the Kiamichi's: the *Kashehotopolo*—Man Deer—who ran ahead of hunters to scare game away, the *Nalusa Chito*—a large black monster who ate solitary hikers, the *Bohpoli*—Throwers—who made strange noises in the forest and sometimes kidnapped children.

Mom worried about monsters the way Tommy Hotabee worried about snipers.

Ghosts, monsters, and men with guns. The history of the world as told to Lizbeth by almost everyone. Most of the time she didn't think about it much, except when she was alone and strange noises followed her like ghostly footsteps of Choctaw who walked all the way from Mississippi.

Alone, the way she was right then.

The sun rose higher as Lizbeth walked through the forest. The hills disappeared as she moved into them. The Kiamichi mountains hid in the trees. No sign she was climbing a mountain except for a gradual change in elevation that wore her enthusiasm down, the way a stream wears creases into stones.

"The impact site," her dad called it. He talked like a scientist but still planted his crops by the signs.

The impact site looked close last night. Now it was invisible. Hidden among oak trees and rocks like white tail deer in hunting season. No broken limbs. No smoldering fire. No hole in the mountain where the shooting star scattered rocks and chunks of caliche clay. Lizbeth couldn't be sure she was on the right mountain. Couldn't see her house behind her. There was no way to know she hadn't wandered onto a false path.

As the sun moved overhead, Lizbeth's shadow shrank into a puddle of darkness at her feet. Animal noises and motions caught her attention, made her remember stories about black bear and cougars and timber wolves and rattle snakes. Real things in the real world that could carry a Choctaw girl away with no help from made-up monsters.

"At least there are no German soldiers," Lizbeth said out loud. It was a perfect time to chase her fears away with smoked ham and homemade bread. No need to be afraid as long as someone was waiting for her back home. As long as she had parents who loved her and friends—even broken ones like Tommy Hotabee—who wanted to see her again.

As Lizbeth ate her lunch she heard the musical sound of water running through rocks. Endless, almost repetitive, soothing as a lullaby. Water music washed her mind clear.

Empty stomachs lead to bad decisions, Lizbeth's mother told her. What about empty minds? She fell asleep dreaming of crystal clear water seeping through fissures in the earth. Persistent, relentless, providing the essence of life since the world began.

A babbling brook, like the babbling of an infant who has no words but still makes his message clear.

"One of us."

If Lizbeth had not been half asleep she wouldn't have understood.

"One of us."

She walked toward the water noise that blended perfectly with animal sounds and wind and the whispers of Choctaw spirits. No wonder her people believed the forest and the mountains were alive.

"One of us." Lizbeth repeated the words, imitated the sound of bubbles with her voice. She didn't have it right quite, but with practice …

Lowland ponds were filled with duckweed and algae. Clots of mud and moss hid everything beneath the surface, but mountain pools were windows into another world. A dark, bottomless spirit-world distorted by ripples from spring water dribbling in and waterfalls splattering out, feeding plants along a slope that ran into a mountain meadow.

Who could blame Lizbeth for folding her clothing into a neat pile and lowering herself into the pool? She floated on her back with her eyes on blue sky and white clouds that changed into memories of things that happened in this place right after the world was made.

Her ears filled with water and the water filled with sound. Noise at first, then real words from a real language. A chant that Lizbeth knew was sung at this pool's edge before people knew the earth was a round ball of rock and dirt circling the sun.

She exhaled, and felt her body sink.

"One of us."

She rotated so she was face down in the pool and sank deeper. No need to breathe—as if she absorbed oxygen through her skin. Perhaps that happened when a girl was called into a mountain pool by ...

Okowa Nahalo. Lizbeth knew that's who had spoken to her. White Water-people. Spirits who lured children into the water where they became "one of us" or drowned. Either way, no one ever saw them alive again.

"One of us."

White luminescent dots floated in the darkness below her. Punctuation marks at the end of her life. They swarmed like bees among the rocks and plants growing at the bottom of the pool. Illuminated the shadows with their spirit-light so Lizbeth could see what lay there. Bones. Ribs and vertebrae in a random pattern like the ones old-time Choctaw holy men tossed on the ground to predict the future.

Bones attract the soul. That's what the elders believed. They saved their ancestors bones in bags and boxes. Stored them in bone houses so the ancestors would stay close. Drawn to their skeletons the way iron is drawn to a magnet.

This was a human skeleton at the bottom of the shadow. A single human skeleton scattered by fish and water currents. A girl Lizbeth's age—not lured to her death by the White Water-people, but murdered at the edge of this mountain pool. Her body weighted down with rocks and tossed into the deepest darkest part where her skeleton was picked clean. Where her only company were the *Okowa Nahalo.*

"Not for us." Spoken by the glittering dots.

Lizbeth didn't know if they were talking about her or the girl who'd been waiting at the bottom of the pool for a thousand years. The dead girl whose spirit couldn't leave until she told someone what happened here.

Things Lizbeth didn't want to hear but she listened anyway. Foreign words so full of emotion their meaning was clear. The girl's face rose from the bottom of the pool like colored smoke from a ritual fire. Back lit by the White Water-people flitting behind her like specks of burning dust falling from the sky.

"Like tracer bullets," The words came out in bubbles as Lizbeth spoke.

The White Water-people backed away but the spirit girl kept talking until her story was finished. Then the face in front of Lizbeth faded.

An image remained after the face was gone. Like the after-image of a lightning flash. Changing colors, changing shape like a bud blooming into a flower.

Tommy Hotabee's face took the place of the spirit girl's. His lips moved: "You've got the healing touch, Lizzy."

His face dissolved into a cloud of *Okowa Nahalo* sparks. They flashed in different directions like the Perseid Meteor Shower.

"Not for us. Chosen. A healer."

Lizbeth looked at the hand that touched Tommy Hotabee and took his pain away. Transparent. Like a sculpture made of ice. The White Water-people swam behind her fingers and lit them like the Neon signs she saw once when her family took her to Tulsa.

Her other hand was transparent, too, and her legs. Her hair floated in front of her eyes like spun glass, not invisible because it sparkled with the hidden colors of sunlight as she rose to the top of the mountain pool.

Voices followed her to the surface.

"Not for us," they said. "But we can use her in another way."

A ghost. What else could she be? A Choctaw girl whose shadow is a rainbow. Lizbeth's transparent body broke the sunlight like a prism. It painted rocks with color when she moved.

Do ghosts feel sharp rocks on the soles of their bare feet? Do they feel the wind in their hair? Lizbeth pinched herself. Solid flesh and pain. Two very unghostly things. She couldn't go home like this. Her parents would run from the house. Her friends too. Even Tommy Hotabee wouldn't want to be around her.

The only people who might be interested in a Choctaw girl made of glass would be white scientists. The ones who invented radios and automobiles and bombs strong enough to blow the world apart.

Lizbeth sat on a stone beside the pool and cried. Her tears were transparent—exactly like they were before. At least something was still the same.

The sun and wind were still the same too. They felt the same as they evaporated the water on Lizbeth's skin. Warmed and cooled her at the same time like when she stepped out of a bathtub on a summer day when the windows were open.

The color came back into her skin as the water evaporated. In pastel splotches at first, but after a while it all came back, exactly as it had been before she was almost "one of us".

Lizbeth looked into the pool of water. She could still see the little specks of light swimming below the surface. She retrieved her Mason jar, emptied it, and refilled it with the spirit-water. Held it in the sun, and watched the *Okowa Nahalo* swim in circles.

... use her in another way.

She'd take the water home, show her parents the miracle in the mason jar. Better than a rock that fell out of the sky. Maybe her father would find a scientific name for the White Water-people in the *Farmer's Almanac*.

Science and Choctaw spirits in the same Mason jar.

"Water bugs," dad told Lizbeth.

"Stuff and nonsense." Mom didn't see anything in the water at all. Lizzy supposed spirits were something people talked about but didn't like to hold in their hands.

"Little dots of light," Lizbeth told them. "Swimming in pairs, like ..." she stopped before she said, *"eyes from the spirit world."*

Didn't stop herself, exactly. Her lips and tongue went numb in the middle of the sentence. Her mind went blank the way it did sometimes when she stood up too fast. Lizbeth reminded herself to breath. Then she reminded herself to breath slowly.

The little pairs of spirit eyes watched her from the edge of the Mason jar. They didn't move when she swirled the water. Mom and dad weren't looking for specks in the water anymore, they looked at Lizbeth.

"Don't make such a fuss over a jar full of bubbles, Lizzy." Mom put the back of her hand on Lizbeth's forehead. "You don't feel hot."

If dad hadn't been there, mom would have gotten more personal. She'd ask Lizbeth about bowel movements, the color of her urine, whether she'd finally gotten her period. But since dad was there—luckily—all she said was: "Maybe you should pay a visit to Miss MacAlvin.

"I don't need a healing woman." Lizbeth had no idea what Miss MacAlvin would say about a jar full of *Okowa Nahalo*. She was an old-time Choctaw healer, so maybe she really believed in spells and spirits. More likely, she'd prescribe some kind of herbal tea that tasted the way a skunk smelled.

Miss MacAlvin was big on purges. Concoctions and decoctions that stirred up her patients' insides the way Hitler stirred up the Germans. If she couldn't think of an herb or plant remedy for something, she was likely to recommend a four-day fast followed by a steam ritual. She'd been known to recommend that people burn their clothing, shoot their dogs, and sleep naked with river stones under their pillows. When Lizbeth's friend, Nancy Anotubby, missed too much school because of headaches and stomach cramps, Miss MacAlvin said all she needed was a good whipping. It must have worked because Nancy never missed any more school after her mother followed the healing woman's advice.

If Lizbeth's mom and dad didn't see the *Okowa Nahalo* swimming in the water, it was a sure thing they wouldn't believe her story about how she'd turned transparent and how didn't need to breath while she floated under water and released a little dead girl's trapped spirit. If she told her parents that story, they wouldn't be talking about a healing woman; they'd be talking about a mental hospital in Tulsa where white doctors filled crazy Choctaw girls full of electricity and stuck needles into their brains.

So Lizzy told mom and dad they were right. "Bubbles and waterbugs. That's probably all they are." She promised to throw the water away, and she tried, but she could only spill a drop of two before her mind went numb again and she found herself walking into her bedroom and sliding the Mason jar underneath her bed.

We can use her in another way. The words bubbled through her mind and left her tingling all over. As if the white doctors had already charged her with electricity.

She sat beside her bed and listened to the noises coming from the jar. Quick sharp voices like squirrels chattering, but chattering in a real language full of strange vowels and consonants Lizbeth had never heard before. They were talking about her. Talking about her parents. Talking about friends of hers who they had never met, but wanted to.

"Sea monkeys," Olivia Lewis decided the second she looked into the jar. She pinky-swore to keep Lizbeth's secret and proved she could do it by sharing secrets she was keeping for three of her other friends.

Olivia had read about sea monkeys in a Dell Comic Book. "*Superman*," she told Lizzy as if that made a difference. "You order sea monkey eggs from the comic book, and when they hatch out you have a bunch of little underwater monkeys."

She slid the jar back into its hiding place underneath Lizbeth's bed and suggested they do something else now that the mystery was solved.

"I didn't order sea monkey eggs from a comic book." Lizbeth had only seen comic books from a distance once when her mother took her to the Rexall drugstore in Idabel. "This water came from a spring fed mountain pool about a mile from here."

"Wild sea monkeys." Olivia had an explanation for everything.

Lizbeth showed the jar of water spirits to several of her friends before the summer ended. They all promised not to tell—but none of them kept their promises. Some of them saw nothing, like her mother. Some of them saw water bugs, like her dad. The ones with comic books saw sea monkeys, like Olivia Lewis. By the time school started, everybody knew about Lizbeth's jar of spirits.

When Tommy Hotabee came over to see the wild sea monkeys, Lizzy asked him where he heard the story.

"Don't know, exactly," Tommy said. "Everybody's talking about it."

Since Tommy didn't have any real friends except for Lizbeth, she knew *everybody* really was talking about it.

He held the jar to the light and swirled the water.

"Ain't sea monkeys." Tommy peered into the water like a gypsy fortuneteller searching for the future in a crystal ball.

"Sea monkeys are really brine shrimp," he said. "Nothin' special at all. These things swim around in pairs."

Tommy's eyes crossed a little. He mumbled something Lizbeth couldn't understand, but she thought he might be saying, "one of us."

"Tommy." She put the back of her hand on his forehead like her mother had done when Lizzy had been trying to show her the spirits in the water. "*Okowa Nahalo,*" she said. "You know, White Water-people."

Tommy's eyes went back to normal. Maybe Lizzy's touch had done that, or maybe the spirits had decided he wasn't "one of us". Because even though Tommy saw them clearly, even though he heard their thoughts, the *Okowa Nahalo* didn't want him. Didn't have a use for him the way the U.S. Army didn't have a use for him once he'd been crippled.

"They look kind of like Messerschmitts," he said—normal voice, not dreamy anymore. "Maybe Mustangs."

"Horses?" Lizzy brought him out of it all the way with a kiss on the cheek.

"Airplanes," Tommy said. "They chased each other across the skies. Carried bombs on their wings sometimes, but most of them were fighters."

Lizbeth took the jar of water spirits and slid it under her bed. Kissed Tommy on the cheek again. Her mother would have been more concerned about that than about wild sea monkey spirits that could hold your thoughts the way a child holds the string of a balloon.

Tommy's thoughts floated away from the White water-people high above the earth and he could see all the way to Europe where the war was still going on. Lizbeth walked him to the door before the war took hold of him again. Took him outside beyond the reach of the spirits in the jar.

While she held his hand, Tommy didn't limp.

"Headache's gone," he told her. "Had that headache since meteor shower night. Now it's gone." He told Lizbeth once again, "No use denying it. You've got the healing touch."

Lizbeth thought it was her idea to carry around her jar of water spirits until she tried to pour the water on the ground but couldn't make it slosh over the rim of the jar. Then she tried to store it in the shed behind her house, so she wouldn't have it in her room. So she wouldn't wake up spell stuck.

But she found the jar under her bed every morning, and when Lizbeth looked in the mirror her eyes looked like Tommy Hotabee's when he was almost "one of us".

The White Water-people made Lizzy carry that jar around to everyone she knew. Looking for someone who suited them. They didn't want Tommy Hotabee because he was crippled and they couldn't have Lizbeth because she was chosen for another purpose.

But they wouldn't let her mind go, either. Lizbeth knew that for sure after her mother volunteered her to babysit for their friends from church.

"My name is Iris." The little girl was five years old. "Flower name." Iris held the door open for Lizbeth. "All my friends have flower names." Iris was full of information that wouldn't wait until Lizbeth hung her coat in the hall closet and said hello to the little girl's parents.

Iris's mom and dad were in a hurry to go somewhere. Lizbeth didn't ask when they'd be coming back because if they stuck around very long they'd want to know why she was carrying a jar of water. Lizzy had an excuse ready. Had a lot of excuses, depending on how much they'd already heard. But Iris's parents didn't have time to wonder about the witch-girl with the strange look and the Mason jar.

"Cold outside," Iris's mother said.

"Getting colder," her father said.

Iris told them it was because Christmas would be coming soon and there had to be lots of snow for Santa's sled. She stood in the door and waved goodbye and when her parents were gone she asked, "What's in the jar, Lizzy?"

Lizbeth handed the jar to Iris. "Careful, it's very special water."

The house was heated with cast iron stove banked with coal trucked in from the MacAlester mines. Iris sat on an overstuffed couched as close to the heat as she could get.

Lizbeth watched the sea monkeys swim faster. Quick circles, like they were caught in a whirlpool. Their voices weren't loud enough to hear, but Lizzy knew they were talking. They liked the heat. They liked Iris.

"What are they saying, Lizzy?" The little girl held the jar to her ear. She nodded her head as if she agreed to something.

"They want a sister with a flower name." Iris smiled. She placed the rim of the Mason jar on her lips, and swallowed.

Four quick shallow swallows—a sacred number naturally. Lizbeth had plenty of time to stop her. To pull the jar away, but her arms drooped at her sides like a marionette with broken strings.

This was the way the *Okowa Nahalo* reproduced. Took human

children. Changed them. Would Iris's skin turn clear or was that something that only happened in mountain pools? Would she run away from home, jump into the Kiamichi River and turn into a wild sea monkey the way caterpillars turned into butterflies?

"I …" Lizbeth tried to say the little girl's name, but everything past the first letter stuck in her throat.

Better her than me. Not a thought Lizzy wanted, but there it was. She'd handed Iris the jar of spirit water, pretended it was harmless, watched her drink it without any protest past the letter, "I …"

Lizbeth took a deep breath. The way a swimmer does when she's going to dive into cold water and doesn't know how long she'll be under.

"Iri …" Maybe she could have forced it out this time—after it was already too late—but before she could finish, the White Water-people loosened their grip on Lizbeth long enough to shriek. A dog-whistle tone beyond the range of human hearing but it still hurt Lizbeth's ears.

Dogs and coyotes howled in response. Windowpanes vibrated. Glasses rattled in the cupboard.

"*Yali!*" the White Water-people screamed.

A Choctaw word. Lizbeth didn't know much Choctaw, but this word meant, "*I weep.*"

Something mourners cried out at funerals along the Trail of Tears when they were marched to Oklahoma so quickly they weren't allowed to collect the bones of their dead.

"*This one is dying.*" Another scream. Quieter than the first. Not in English, but Lizbeth understood.

Iris spit the last swallow of water back into the jar. She handed it to Lizbeth.

"I'm cold, Lizzy." The little girl's lips were blue. She placed her hands between her legs, folded her shoulders, squeezed herself into a ball and shivered. "I need a blanket please."

Lizbeth put the jar on the floor. She should have thrown it out. Perhaps she would do that later, but now, she wrapped an afghan around Iris's shoulders. Hugged her tight enough to soak up the cold. Rubbed the little girl's hands until her nail beds turned from blue to pink.

"Sorry, Iris," She kissed the little girl on the forehead. Watched the color come back to her cheeks.

"Not your fault, Lizzy. It happens all the time."

Lizbeth could hear the White Water-people chattering in the jar. Excited by the heat from the coal stove. Afraid of what was sure to happen next. They knew the little girl would die within the month. Something that was in her blood, or maybe something her blood should have but didn't. She would die and the spirit specks she'd swallowed would die with her. No way they could escape. Not once they were inside a dying child.

"I feel better Lizzy. You've got the healing touch," she said. Just like Tommy Hotabee.

Lizbeth kissed Iris again. The way a mother kisses a baby who's about to fall asleep, so love will be her last conscious thought.

Lizzy's healing touch wouldn't be good enough. Miss MacAlvin's herbal teas wouldn't help either. Or white doctors' medicine from the Rexall in Idabel. The only thing Lizbeth could do was comfort the little girl and cry along with the spirits in the jar.

"Yali," Lizbeth said.

"What's that mean, Lizzy?"

"Nothing important, Iris. Just something the Choctaw people

say when they can't think of anything else." She sounded like her mother.

Lizbeth told Iris's dad she didn't want a ride back home. "I've been cooped up in warm houses all day long. A walk in the night air will do me good."

"It's freezing out there," Iris's father said. "What will your parents think of us?"

Lizzy knew he wouldn't put up much of a fight. His little girl was ready for bed. Gasoline was rationed.

"It's not cold. It's … bracing." Words like *bracing* always did the trick. Convinced grown-ups they were dealing with somebody smart. Way too smart to get into trouble during a short walk on a long December night when it was too cold for anybody bad to be outside. Too cold for robbers and murderers and German snipers. Too cold for Choctaw monsters. That's what *bracing* meant.

He looked at the jar Lizbeth carried but only for a moment. She told him, "Waterbugs. It's a school science project."

"Aha." He looked like he had his doubts, but he didn't have any more to say.

Lizbeth thought he might have a great deal to say if he knew she'd let Iris drink water from that jar. That his daughter was part of her *science project*. That she was going to die soon and there was nothing anyone could do to stop it.

The cold night air swept Lizzy's hair back as she walked out the door. It felt good against her skin. Cold enough to make her nose crackle when she breathed. *Bracing,* just like she told Iris's father.

A twenty-minute walk under a cold clear December night sky.

The Choctaw people had walked hundreds of miles on nights much worse than this. She walked past the little clusters of small farms scattered along on the country road. An Indian road still traveled by men on horseback and women in wagons.

Most of the Choctaw had cars now, and tractors that ran on rationed gasoline. Except for that, things hadn't changed so much since this part of Oklahoma was given to the Choctaw for as long as the grass grew and the wind blew.

The wind always blew in Lizbeth's part of the world, but grass season was over for the moment. Green things looked dead, but they'd come back in springtime. Lizbeth held the cold jar of water up so she could watch the White Water-people in the moonlight. Everything slows down in the winter, even evil spirits.

The *Okowa Nahalo* didn't like the cold any more than they liked Iris. Lizbeth could feel their complaints vibrating through the glass. Not strong, the way they were in Iris's house. The thoughts came slower—weaker—but they still came.

Most of the houses along the country road had wells in the front yard. Some of the wells had pumps, but most of the families drew water by the bucketful. The White Water-people were still strong enough to make Lizbeth stop and look down every well she passed.

She held the *Okowa Nahalo* over the pools of water at the bottom of the circular stone lined holes. The moon reflected from the surface of the water with an image of Lizbeth's hand holding a jar of evil Choctaw spirits, ready to pour at their command, when they found a well that connected to the right aquifer. They argued like red winged blackbirds fighting over the best tree.

This one was too shallow. That one touched a vein of coal. Too close to a latrine. Downhill from a pigpen. When they found the right well, they would order her to pour the water in. When spring came, they'd lure children into the wells and drainages. Reproduce in their spirit-way until they were ready to follow the underground streams all over the valley.

Could they travel as far the Kiamichi River? The Little River? Further?

If the *Okwa Nahalo* had been warm they could have kept their plans from Lizbeth. They could have blanked her mind, filled her with so much confusion she'd use all her concentration walking and breathing and finding her way back home. The White Water-people still had a firm hold on her but they couldn't shut her out. Couldn't stop her from wondering if there was some way she could stop them.

"The Moon's house is very clean tonight." Lizbeth saw Miss MacAlvin's reflection standing beside hers at the bottom of the well. The healing woman's voice was soft. Her footsteps must have been soft, too, because Lizzy never heard her coming. The *Okowa Nahalo* vibrated. Miss MacAlvin had surprised them too.

Lizbeth realized she was holding the spirit jar over the healing woman's well. No objection, so far. Did Miss MacAlvin understand what she was doing?

"Our ancestors ruled over a great empire," Miss MacAlvin said. "They understood rivers very well." Every time Lizzy had spoken to Miss MacAlvin, the healing woman told a story. Something about the Choctaw, usually before the force-march to Oklahoma.

"I was just …" How would Lizbeth explain what she was just doing. She was just about to infect the entire Southeastern corner of the state with evil spirits, but it wasn't her fault, exactly, because she'd been spell-struck ever since that day in the mountain pool.

Miss MacAlvin put her hand on Lizbeth's shoulder. Stopped the lie in progress. She didn't want an explanation. She wanted Lizbeth to listen like a proper Choctaw girl at story-telling time.

"I'm talking about the days before Christianity, Lizzy, when the ancestors followed the wisdom of the sun."

Lizbeth knew a little something about the ancestors. Not as much as her parents and certainly not as much as the older Choctaw. The schools discouraged learning too many of the old ways. That was left for the elders to teach, so every generation knew a little less than the one that came before.

"The sun and the moon were husband and wife," Miss MacAlvin said. "The stars were their children." She made a sweeping gesture that took in the entire night sky. At that moment, Lizbeth forgot about the *Okwa Nahola*. She still felt the vibrations in the glass but the healing woman's story drowned out their thoughts.

"It's a very big family. Do you see Lizzy?"

She gave Lizbeth a few seconds to consider a family so large no one could count them all. "Most of the brothers and sisters are good and thoughtful children."

Miss MacAlvin looked directly into Lizbeth's eyes, something Choctaw people seldom did. Twin moons reflected from her pupils. A pair of lights looking into Lizzy's soul the way the floating spirit specks in her Mason jar did when the water was warmer.

"But some of the star children are very bad, Lizbeth. A few of them are evil."

Lizbeth thought about the shooting star that fell into the mountains. The one she was looking far when she found the *Okwa Nahola*. Miss MacAlvin smiled. As if she heard that thought—the way Lizzy heard the thoughts of the White Water-people.

"Our ancestors believed the evil children in the sky fell down to earth and changed to spirit creatures. Christian Choctaw call them fallen angels."

Lizbeth pulled the jar away from the well. Held it at her side, away from her body so it couldn't absorb her warmth. The vibrations in the glass had slowed to a tremble. Like a cat purring in Lizzy's hand. Like a cold cat that's gone stiff in the December weather and has to be content to lie still and wait until things change.

The healing woman put both hands on Lizbeth's shoulders. Her

hands radiated warmth that ran down Lizzy's arms and stopped at the wrists so the *Okowa Nahalo* weren't heated up again. Something Lizbeth imagined? Something that happened by accident? Something the Healing Woman knew how to do?

"The ancestors were wrong about many things, Lizbeth. But they understood the dangers of mixing with spirits.

Lizbeth held out the jar of water spirits hoping Miss MacAlvin would take it from her. But the healing woman stepped back. "No one's given a burden too heavy to carry," she said. "Not even that Mason jar. But when things start happening around here, you'll get the blame. Lizzy is bad luck,t hat's what they'll say. Lizbeth is a bad-luck woman."

"What do I do, Miss MacAlvin? What comes next?"

"Use the old ways to solve new problems," the Healing Woman told Lizbeth. Then she turned and walked back to her house.

"What does that mean?" Lizbeth held the Mason jar up to the moonlight. The White Water-people were dead still. A thin slush of ice floated at the top of the jar. Lizbeth held the spirits at arms length as she walked back home, touched the jar only with her fingertips. Now she could put it into the shed behind her house. Maybe she could come up with an old solution to this new problem before the weather warmed again.

Old legends said fire was a gift to the Choctaw from the sun to compensate for man's weakness compared to other creatures. But fire was also a spy.

Lizzy's mother told her, "Careful what you say, the fire will tell on you." Fire heard everything. What you said and even what you only thought.

That's why candles carried birthday wishes all the way to heaven.

That's why the great chiefs smoked promises on a ceremonial pipe.

That's why food offerings were burned.

Fire burned diseases from pots and pans. It cleared fields. It chased cold and darkness into the shadows. Lizbeth had seen fires at every Choctaw ceremony since she was a tiny child. Fires to celebrate the first corn of the season. Fires when a man and a woman married. Fires for births and deaths. Fires for solstices and equinoxes. Some ceremonial fires could be started by anyone. Others required a ceremonial fire maker.

Luak Falaya was the most important fire ceremony of all. The Long Fire, started from a coal descended from the first fire given to the Choctaw by the sun. It was never allowed to go out, even on the Trail of Tears, when people lost everything. When they weren't allowed to sleep, or bury their dead. The people nurtured the fire even while they starved. Embers were always kept alive.

At the end of the year, those embers were used to start a new fire that would be sustained for the next twelve months. The long fire burned tinder, wood, and bad feelings. Lizbeth had never gone to a *Luak Falaya* ceremony, but she'd heard about them from her parents. When she told them she was going with Miss MacAlvin, they couldn't refuse.

So Lizbeth stood beside the healing woman in the cold early hours of the morning and watched the fire keeper pile tinder between the four logs that would support the sacred blaze.

Choctaw gathered in a close circle for warmth and to be part of something that had been going on since the beginning of time. Lizzy was the youngest person there, but her elders moved aside so she could stand close. She and Miss MacAlvin.

Everyone had heard the stories about the young girl who was never seen without her Mason jar. Was it a magic elixir that would change her into an owl? Did she plan to poison their wells, kill their livestock, murder their children and grandchildren?

Lizbeth held the jar close to her chest and watched the fire keeper blow on the sacred embers until the kindling caught fire. He made a short speech, slow and solemn like a prayer. English mixed with Choctaw, spoken in a voice so soft Lizzy could only make out a few words.

The fire burned higher, spread from the dry tinder to the four seasoned logs that would swallow up all the bad feelings of the little Choctaw town. Lizbeth felt the heat on her face, and knew the White Water-people felt it too. She hoped the ceremony would move fast enough so she could finish what she had to do before the water spirits ruled her mind again.

An old man stepped forward. He removed a letter from an envelope and tossed both into the fire. A younger man stepped out of the crowd and embraced him. They wept.

"The old man is Simpson Cross," Miss MacAlvin told Lizzy. "He's burned a hateful letter written by his son Samuel." Their argument turned to smoke and was carried away by the wind.

Other people tossed things onto the fire. A document, a fence stake, the branch of a tree, a broken glass. Symbols of feuds among friends and family members that would end in the heat of the Long Fire.

Lizzy felt her feet trying to edge away from the fire. The Mason jar vibrated in her hands. The water spirits were waking up. Thinking thoughts Lizbeth could hear. Ready to start up again where the cold temperatures had stopped them.

"They've picked a well for their new home," Lizzy said out loud. She started to back away from the fire, but people had crowded in too close.

"Hey there, Lizzy."

She backed into Tommy Hotabee. He put a hand on her right shoulder. Pushed her gently toward the fire.

"Miss MacAlvin told me I should come." Tommy's fingers trembled on her shoulder. Vibrated like the spirits in the Mason jar.

"Said I should stand close so you could lean on me the way I've leaned on you."

The trembling wasn't coming from Tommy's fingers after all. It came from Lizbeth. Every muscle in her body tried to come to a decision—whether to run away or stay and fight. The same decision soldiers and healing women have been making since time began.

"You know what you have to do, Lizbeth," Miss MacAlvin said. "You're strong enough."

Lizbeth had never had much confidence in prayer, but it worked for her in the heat of the Long Fire with Tommy standing behind her. Miss MacAlvin standing at her side. The people around Lizzy prayed. Some chanted Choctaw words. Some sang Christian hymns. It didn't matter. They were there for Lizbeth. Lisbeth was there for them.

She stepped forward and spilled the jar into the fire.

A bright flash, like a meteorite striking the side of a mountain. Everyone was blinded for a moment. Yellow spots floating in front of them made it hard to see the white cloud of smoke rising into the morning sky.

They heard the cry of barn owls fading into the distance. A sure sign of something evil leaving.

An old man said, "Lizbeth's thrown away her magic."

"*Nahullo!*" an old woman shouted.

"Lizbeth *nahullo!*" Other people joined in.

"Sacred," Miss MacAlvin said. "That's what it means." She stood on one side of Lizbeth; Tommy Hotabee moved to her other side. His injured leg made him lean against her for support.

When she took his hand he stood up straight and smiled. Tommy removed something from his pocket and tossed it into the fire. Lizzy watched it disappear into the ashes.

"The bullet they took from my leg," he said. "Now it's got no hold on me."

Lizbeth squeezed his hand a little harder. Tommy squeezed back. Everyone in the Long Fire Circle joined hands. Strength and confidence flowed through Lizzy like water under pressure.

"The healing touch," she said. "I guess it works both ways."

Messages
by Rory Donahoe

a NOVEMBER BREEZE SWEPT over Henry and he instinctively held a paper cup full of warm coffee just a bit closer to his chest. He had been standing in line for nearly twelve hours. Morning broke slowly, and he watched beams of piercing morning light shine down the street and reflect brightly off of store windows.

Henry took a sip and allowed the hot steam to warm his face. He couldn't leave his spot, so he had bought the coffee from a vendor walking down the line. Henry wished he had offered him cream, but the warmth and much-needed caffeine were good enough.

Henry glanced down at his phone to help pass the time.

"What does it say?" came a soft voice from behind him.

Henry turned around. "Excuse me?"

"You checked the time, right? What time is it?" asked a girl wrapped in a big purple scarf and a heavy winter coat. She appeared to be in her early twenties, like Henry.

"Uh, it's about six."

"Then the sun's about to come up, thank goodness! It's way too cold." The girl thrust her mittened hand out to Henry. "My name is Georgia, what's yours?"

Henry held out his right hand, and realized he was still holding

About the Author

Rory Donahoe is a writer and illustrator who splits his time between Salt Lake City and San Francisco. If you find him, he'll most likely be pondering the depths of the human condition until he eventually gives up and makes nachos.

the coffee. Georgia's face brightened as Henry fumbled with the cup until he finally shook her hand. "My name's Henry."

"So, what do you think, Henry? Will the device really work?" asked Georgia.

Henry looked toward the front of the line and couldn't make out where it started: a thousand bodies all collected into an endless swarm of people, all pressing forward, all buzzing with the same nervous excitement.

"I don't know," Henry replied. "I hope it works, if just to make all this waiting worth it."

Georgia sat down, and Henry followed suit. Finishing the last sip of his coffee, Henry sat the empty cup down beside him; the emerging sun had taken away some of the chill.

"I heard the device can record your thoughts, even your dreams! Can you imagine? Waking up and watching your dreams?" asked Georgia.

Henry looked at her, her face tucked safely in the hood of her jacket. "I think the device can do a lot of amazing things, but I think there's one reason all of these people are here—the messages."

The device was an amazing new gadget designed to sync to the brainwaves of its user. Think of a face, the device could call that person. Dictate a message by thought, then save it or send it. Set reminders for important events simply by focusing on the date and time.

As amazing as those innovations were, they weren't what had millions of people across the world lined up to get one. It was what would happen in twenty years, by some not-yet-developed quirk in future versions of the device.

What would I say, thought Henry, *if I had the chance to say something to my past self?* Twenty years ago, Henry would have been five years old. What information would a five-year-old need to know—what would a five-year-old understand about a world so far off?

"I'm sure you're right," said Georgia fiddling with the tassels of her jacket. "What do you think yours will say?"

"Just hope it's not stock tips!" said a man walking by. He was wearing a pressed blue suit beneath a long black coat. "I've spent the last day waiting in this stupid line, and I'm sick of it. My associates in New York have told me that they're all getting the same information, and stocks have exploded. Buy this, or sell that … now all of those stocks are nearly a thousand dollars a share; it's insanity! Don't even get me started on the lottery, several million winners today, leaving just pennies for each person."

"Did anyone you know get something besides financial tips?" asked Georgia.

The businessman stood straight and appeared to calm a bit, and adjusted his collar. "A friend of mine said he was given a date with the message to turn right instead of left. How is that supposed to make someone feel, forever wondering what you're trying to avoid? If that's not enough to drive a man insane I don't know what is. This isn't for me, the future isn't supposed to be known … that's why it's the future!" He threw his hands in the air and stormed off, cursing to himself under his breath.

Georgia turned to Henry. "Maybe his friend still can turn left, and maybe he should. Some people are saying that there will be a new timeline, one different from the people who sent the messages. Or hey," said Georgia with a smirk, "maybe turning right will make things worse."

Henry fell back into his head and tried to envision each tiny step in his life that could have been different, each time he could have turned right instead of left, and how much his life would change. He thought back to every poor decision—the time he crashed his dad's car, the moment he dropped out of college, and when he broke a girl's heart. It made his stomach sink and his head ache.

"I guess I just hope mine isn't lottery numbers," said Henry, forcing a smile. "What about you? What soaring and infinite wisdom are you hoping to have sent yourself?"

Georgia looked up to the sky and contemplated the question as if the answer lay deep inside her. "I kind of want to know if I'll ever make it with my art, or … well, I just hope she tells me she found the courage to be happy."

Georgia paused and took a deep breath, "I applied to some art schools, but I was rejected. It hurts, you know, to hear that something you're passionate about maybe isn't what you should be doing. I want to know that they were wrong, and I guess I'm just looking for permission to keep going." Georgia closed her eyes and turned away.

Henry, now uncomfortable, rubbed the back of his neck. He hadn't meant to upset her. Hearing Georgia's story reminded him that he wasn't sure what he wanted his message to say. There were so many people, all sorts of people, all hoping for something. Some would want success, or fame, or money, or love. Everyone was looking for a dose of clarity in a sea of uncertainty—a way to escape the fear of the unknown.

Henry could hear the rustling of people standing up echo off the buildings across the street. He looked ahead—the line was so long, he could hear people moving before he could see them. He waited until the people in front of him got up, and then he rose behind them. And like one great wave it continued behind him and out of sight.

The next few hours of waiting were agonizing. From what he understood, the store had to calibrate each device by putting a hood filled with diodes, lights, and receptors on each person's head. Once the device was synced up to the user's brainwaves, it would begin to receive information. And in just two decades from today, users would be able to send a thought, a short and simple sentence, back to their devices—all of their devices. The messages didn't travel through time, but instead existed at a higher state where the past, present, and future occurred simultaneously.

Henry and Georgia watched as people passed by, their faces grim. "Why do they look so sad? What did their messages say?" said Georgia. A man and woman with linked arms overheard. The man stopped dead in his tracks and looked back at her, his eyes red from barely restrained tears.

"My wife's message said 'leave him before the cancer,'" said the man somberly.

"What did yours say?" said Georgia to the man.

"I didn't get one." He turned to the woman beside him. Her expression didn't change and she didn't look back. He looked down, his face cold, and they continued walking again.

Georgia retreated into her jacket, and looked at Henry. "I don't think this is right," said Georgia. She peeled back her hood revealing long locks of curly brown hair, which she shook violently. "Maybe they're right, maybe our future shouldn't be known."

"But I have to know," replied Henry. "You would miss knowing your own future?"

"If it makes me like them, then yes," she said, surveying the crowd of dreary people as they lifelessly marched from the store like mourners at a funeral procession, their hopes and excitement expired.

"Hasn't anyone gotten good news?" asked Henry loudly. His eyes locked on each person as they passed by.

A woman looked up briefly and peered back towards Henry. "These are our mistakes. What could you tell yourself after twenty years that could possibly fix them?" And she continued on.

As news of the messages spread, people started to disperse and the line began to move much faster. "It's only one possible version of future events," some said. Others became fearful they would worry about events that wouldn't occur or, more troubling, act on information that would make matters worse. "Better not to know," they murmured, but didn't sound convinced.

Finally, after nearly a full day of waiting, it was Henry's turn.

Henry stepped through the door apprehensively. The space was bare, stark white and brightly lit, forcing him to shield his eyes. An employee dressed all in white directed him to a chair and sat him down while another accepted his payment. He heard one say that he was placing an electroencephalographer over his head, and his world went dark.

He latched onto the word—electroencephalographer. *The hood*, he thought, and allowed the strange-sounding word to roll through his mind. Slowly, he succumbed to an uncomfortable feeling of claustrophobia coupled with the odd sensation of a million tiny pricks across his scalp. He could feel the pressure of one of the white-clad employee's hands on his shoulder, holding him still.

In the distance he could hear Georgia politely declining a device. Was she the smart one? He thought. Did he really need to know his future? A million questions filled his mind. Will there even be a message? Will I be alive in twenty years? Will it tell me about a future relationship, or maybe a wife? Will it warn me about cancer? Do I have cancer now?

Henry's hands started to sweat. The darkness, the tightening grip on his shoulder, and the fear and uncertainty started to overwhelm him. The pricks began to feel like daggers.

Henry's chair shot up, the hood torn from his face, and he was left noticeably disoriented. "Here you go, sir! Thanks for coming," said a white-clad employee.

Still reeling from the experience, he stumbled out of the store. He looked down at the tiny device, and wondered how such a small thing could cause so much misery. On the screen there flashed a tiny green box.

1 New Message

Henry stuffed the device in his pocket without opening the message. Georgia was sitting on a curb across the street, her arms wrapped around her legs, and her jacket folded beside her. Henry walked over to her.

"Are you all right?"

"I decided not to get one," said Georgia.

"I overheard."

"I've decided that I don't need someone to tell me whether or not I can do what I love. Not a school, and not a silly message. I'm going to do it because it's what I want to do, and my destiny will be decided by me—not by anyone else, and not by a message from

Henry tried to envision each tiny step in his life that could have been different and how much his life would change.

the future," she said. She collected her jacket and looked back up at Henry. "What about you, what did yours say?"

"I didn't look." Henry retrieved the device from his pocket and held it out to her. "Here, you look."

"No, I don't want to," said Georgia, waving it away. "It's a message sent to you, from you. It's not for anyone but you. Plus, I doubt it would make sense to me."

"I kind of hope it is lottery numbers," said Henry, holding the device cautiously in his hands like it was a loaded weapon.

"Read it. You went through all that work! Besides, I need to find a resolution vicariously through you," Georgia smirked.

Henry allowed himself a small laugh, and timidly activated the screen on his device. Again, an alert flashed that he had one message. He raised his finger up to the device slowly and he paused. The moment of doubt proved futile and he clicked the message. He allowed each word its own moment to sink in deeply with the gravity it deserved.

Everything will work out.

"What does it say?" she asked.

"What I needed to hear," said Henry, finally exhaling, allowing himself a satisfactory smile. "Are you hungry? There's a great place to get some breakfast just down the street—I was planning on going there afterwards anyway, and I'd like it if you came along."

"Yeah," replied Georgia, scrunching up her nose and beaming brightly. "I'd like that, too."

Ancestors
by Kayce Guthmiller

Filaments like fiber-optic projector screens lace the
pores of his face,
Knot the joints and little bones:
Replica gears turning with the eloquence and presence
of a flame.
Though the sun may have held his face in its hands for
fewer days,
Unrelenting likeness manifests carbon copy footprints
down a commonly traveled path.
The ghosts of failing cellular processes recreate young
mannerisms I've recognized,
As I know them, Father;
With certain death does not come the end of existence.

About the Poet

Kayce Guthmiller is a junior at Idaho Fine Arts Academy in Eagle, Idaho. Her academic focus is on classical and improvisational music, but she is equally passionate about writing.

Ink to page is soon to decay,
But sticky fuchsia etchings you've made on my mind like
    futile tattoos do not fade.
A legacy takes many forms:
The hourglass heartbeat doesn't always reside in its chest,
But born from yours,
It wears an antique cloak of immortality.

Mutiny's plague is one that dyes your roots black and
    feeds on your photosynthesis.
Paradoxical,
All toxic,
One-sided symbiosis.
Your mouth shapes in the way to harbor sharp words.
Scaffolding on the bones of your hands cause square
    movements in directions you're unsure.
The brain's civil war calls to draft the entirety of you,
The opposing sides are synonymous,
Adorned with searing plum bruises
And shards of a frosted window lying at the floor of the
    dark cage in your chest.

》

It escapes the web of veins confined to your skin
    and syncs with that to which it's similar.
What was once a compassionate touch scars wine
    on both bodies,
The black pit powerfully swells as it reaches its
    threads beyond the host.
External cataracts cloud reality.
Jealousy.

Encrypted in hereditary code,
Self-sabotage is a communicable disease;
It does not biodegrade.
Endemic fossil fuels sew themselves onto oxygen
    molecules,
Toxicity like ink clouds a clear pool.

Intercept the wave of human output.
Interpret the atlas with unadulterated conception
    of North,
Do with your steps what landmarks were thinly
    traced by numb fingertips.
Let the sun leak the universe's secondhand secrets
    on your solar powered skin,
Shed your layers and give the eager light a home.

Remember his face,
How it was poured from a mold only slightly altered,
And know how you place each foot on this Earth,
Each breath you return to the sky,
Should be considered an ancestral heirloom more potent than
blood.

Anywhere but Here
by Stone Showers

ARON SHOULDERED HIS DOOR open as the truck rolled to a stop. Moving slowly, he climbed down out of the cab, then turned and reached back inside for his gear. He was tired. The ride down from Whitehorse had been rough, the road gullied by autumn rains.

"Do you have enough money for food?" The truck driver asked.

Aaron nodded. "I'll be fine," he said.

Three months shy of his sixteenth birthday, Aaron had been on the road for five days. The sum total of his belongings consisted of an old backpack, a few odd mementos and single change of clothes. With the exception of a few small bills, his pockets were empty.

"You sure you're going to be all right?" The driver asked.

Aaron forced a smile. "I'll be fine," he said again.

During the ride down from Whitehorse, Aaron had told the truck driver about the argument with his father and about the night he'd left home. The driver listened politely, nodding occasionally, and in the end finally agreed that Aaron had done the right thing by leaving.

"Life can be hard like that, sometimes," the man had said. Aaron thought about this as he slid his backpack out of the cab.

About the Author

Stone Showers lives in Central Oregon with his wife and two children. His work has recently appeared in or is forthcoming at *Niteblade*, *Stupefying Stories*, *Black Denim Lit* and *Saturday Night Reader*. His short story "The Precipice" appeared in the first issue of *Ember*.

It was early morning in the eastern Yukon, the sun still hidden behind a line of clouds to the east. The tiny village in front of them lay quiet, most of its buildings cloaked in shadow.

"There are good people here," the truck driver told him. "If you have any trouble getting a ride, you go talk to Auntie Grace at the café. She'll take care of you."

Fifty yards off the road, a dilapidated diner huddled next to a stand of black spruce. The café's wooden porch leaned out over a graveled lot riddled with potholes. A single truck sat in front of the building, its rusted bed stacked high with un-split rounds of firewood.

A drop of rain splattered dust at the boy's feet, and then another. Aaron set his gear down in the dirt and tugged a ragged sweatshirt out from under the flap. He thanked the driver for what he'd done, then closed the door and watched as the old man pulled back out onto the highway. Leaves and small twigs skittered back and forth across the road in front of him. As the truck disappeared into the distance, the rain began to come down harder.

Aaron's clothes were soaked through by the time he reached the café's porch. Shivering, he shrugged his backpack to the ground and pulled the dripping sweatshirt off over his head. Heavy drops staccatoed the roof above him. A small bell jangled as Aaron pushed his way through the front door.

"Mornin', sweetie," the waitress said. "You have a nice swim?"

At the far end of the bar the lone customer stifled a laugh. From his perch behind the serving counter, the cook looked out at Aaron and scowled.

"Coffee?" the waitress asked.

Aaron nodded and slid onto a stool at the end of the bar. The inside of the café reminded him of his father's shop. The light fixtures were tarnished brass, the floors faded linoleum. Rusted logging implements hung from the walls as decoration. The old man at the end of the counter turned to look at him.

"You just come down through Whitehorse?" The man asked.

"Came through last night," Aaron said.

The man nodded. "I hear the roads are in bad shape up that way."

"The runoff has carved some deep ruts into the highway," Aaron said. "And there's a bad washout this side of the Yukon."

The man considered this for a moment. Finally, he stood and reached for his jacket. "Hey, Jimmy," he called. "You going to help with that firewood, or do I have to unload it myself?"

Laughing, the cook came out from behind the service counter. "Give me fifty bucks off the price, Sammy, and I'll unload it for you."

The cook lifted a canvas jacket from its hook and pulled it on over his arms. He stood in front of Aaron as he did so, thick fingers fumbling with the buttons of his coat. "Just drinking coffee today?" He asked.

Aaron shrugged. "I just came in to get out of the rain, that's all."

The cook scowled. "This time of year, it rains pretty much all the time," he said. With this, the man followed his friend out into the weather. The door slammed hard behind the two, the small bell banging against the glass.

//

Once the men were gone, the waitress touched a hand to Aaron's arm. "Don't mind Jimmy," she said. "Sometimes it takes him a while to warm up to people."

Aaron watched as the men stepped off the porch and walked together across the parking lot. The two leaned into the wind, hands shoved deep into their pockets. The only sound was the soft stutter of rain against the roof.

"It's quiet here," Aaron said. "Is it always like that?"

The waitress shrugged. "It gets like this near the end of summer," she said. "The tourists are the first to leave, and after that, the so-called residents."

"But you stay on?"

"Someone has to." The waitress wiped at the counter with a rag. "We take care of things here," she said.

Out in the parking lot, the men had climbed into the bed of the pickup. The two stood close together in the belly of the truck, each of them in turn leaning down to grab hold of a round, and then heaving it out over the side.

"Sammy there drives down about once a month with a load of firewood for us," the waitress said. "Without him, I think Jimmy and I would both be frozen solid come spring time."

Aaron smiled at this. He liked the waitress, and realized then that this must be the woman the truck driver had spoken of. Grace looked to be in her mid-forties, hair just beginning to gray at the temples. Laugh lines creased the corners of her eyes.

"I haven't seen you around these parts before," the waitress said. "You just passing through, or do you have family near?"

"Just passing through."

Grace nodded. Outside, Jimmy lifted the last of the firewood and tossed it onto the pile. The rain came down in a steady drizzle now. It dripped off the men's hats, and stained the shoulders of their coats dark. Once again, the waitress touched a hand to Aaron's arm.

"You look so young," she said. "Does your mother know where you are now?"

Aaron glanced at the woman, then quickly away again. "My mother left home when I was a little boy," he said. "The last I heard, she was living in Montana."

Grace frowned at this. Looking past the boy, she watched as her husband accepted a broom from his friend and began to sweep needles and bits of bark toward the back of the truck.

"Is it what you expected?" Grace asked.

"What do you mean?"

"The road," Grace said. "Leaving home. Is it what you expected?"

Aaron thought about this for a moment. He wasn't really sure what he'd expected. "It's lonely."

The waitress nodded. "It all takes a bit of getting used to, doesn't it—the emptiness, I mean?" Grace mopped at the counter with her rag. "When Jimmy and I first moved here I thought I'd go crazy. There was so little to do, so few people to talk to. But Jimmy had always dreamed of owning his own place. He read about this one in the paper just after we got married. We drove up two weeks later to see it." Grace looked out at the two men. Jimmy stood on the front porch now. Sam had climbed back into his truck.

"The diner was everything Jimmy had ever wanted," Grace said. "But I was scared. I never imagined myself living someplace like this."

"Then why did you stay?"

Grace looked at the boy. "What choice did I have?" she asked. "I couldn't ask Jimmy to give up his dream. Could I?"

As Jimmy came back in through the front door, the cook held the bell in his right hand to keep it from jangling. He removed his coat, then lifted his apron and strung the garment back around his waist.

"Still drinking coffee?" he asked.

Aaron nodded. Jimmy looked as if her were about to say something more when Grace stepped between them.

"Leave the boy alone, Jimmy. He hasn't done anything wrong."

"Hasn't he? What do you know about this one, Grace? For that matter, what do you know about any of them? The kids that pass through here—they never stay, do they? They're always on the move, always looking for someplace better." With this, Jimmy turned and ducked back into the kitchen. Aaron could no longer see him, but he could hear the man banging pots and pans together, as if in protest.

"You have to forgive him," Grace said. "He isn't really as mean as he sounds. It's just that life has been hard on us these last couple of years."

Aaron shrugged and looked away. "That's okay," he said. "Everyone has their own problems, I guess."

Grace nodded and dabbed at the counter with her rag. "Do you mind if I ask you something personal?" She said.

Outside, a car passed by on the highway, its fenders caked with mud and dirt. The sun had come out again, and the light shone brightly against the dampened roadway. Aaron felt the waitress watching him, the woman waiting for him to respond. Gentle winds tilted the trees on the opposite side of the parking lot.

"Why did you leave home?" Grace asked. "Was your life really so terrible there?"

Aaron didn't answer right away. Instead, he took a sip of coffee and thought about what the woman had asked. When he did speak, he chose his words carefully.

"My father and I never got along very well," he said. "I don't know why. For some reason we were always arguing. He told me once that I reminded him of my mother. Apparently she and I have the same mannerisms, the same eyes. My father must have hated that—seeing her every time he looked at me."

Downing the last of his coffee, Aaron stood and fished a handful of change out of his pocket.

"Thanks for the coffee," he said. "And for being so kind. I hope everything works out for you."

//

When Aaron stepped onto the front deck, he found Jimmy sitting on a wooden bench to his right. The man held a cigarette between two fingers. Head down, elbows tucked in tight to his body, Jimmy watched smoke curl slowly around his hands.

"It's hard on her," he said. "Seeing kids like you. Tears her up inside." The man turned and looked at Aaron. "I'm just trying to protect her, that's all. You have to understand that."

Aaron knelt next to his backpack and unzipped one of the side pouches. He removed a piece of beef jerky from its package and tore the end off with his teeth.

"I heard what you said in there," Jimmy said. "About you and your father not getting along." The man stood and tossed what was left of his cigarette out into the parking lot. "I don't know what happened between you and him. Ain't none of my business, really. But whatever it was, it don't mean he doesn't care. You understand?"

Aaron nodded. Jimmy stood over the boy for a moment, then turned and stepped off the porch. The man crossed the parking lot to the pile of firewood that he and Sam had unloaded that morning. Jimmy walked slowly, knees never quite straightening. When reached the woodpile he knelt down in the dirt and tipped one of the larger rounds over in front of him. Even from a distance Aaron could see how difficult this was for him. There was pain in the man's movements, hesitation. Without thinking, Aaron stepped down off the porch and quickly crossed the gravel lot. Jimmy looked up at him as he approached.

"You forget something?" The man asked.

"I just thought maybe I could help, that's all."

"And why would you do that?"

Uncomfortable under the man's stare, Aaron searched for something to say. "When I was younger, I used to help my father chop firewood," he said.

Jimmy considered this for a moment. Finally, the man nodded and pushed himself back to his feet. "If you want, I suppose you could stack the pieces there by the porch." Jimmy grabbed an axe from the woodpile and shrugged the handle onto his shoulder. The muscles of his neck and arms strained with the effort.

The two worked for the next half hour in silence, the man chopping, the boy stacking. The morning's rain had cleansed the air and they both breathed deep the scent of pine bark and spruce. Aaron scooped two pieces of firewood from the ground and stacked them onto a pile near the end of the porch. Behind him, Jimmy grunted as he lifted another round onto the chopping block. The man coughed once, and then again. When Aaron turned he found that Jimmy had dropped down to his knees. The man leaned against the chopping block, his breathing suddenly labored.

"Are you okay?" Aaron asked.

Jimmy nodded. His face and neck had both flushed red as he struggled to breath. "Just a bit of asthma, that's all."

Aaron stepped forward and offered to help the man up, but Jimmy shrugged out of his grasp.

"I ain't that feeble," the man wheezed. Using the axe handle to support his weight, Jimmy pushed himself back to his feet. Moving slowly, he sat down on the deck and removed an inhaler from his shirt pocket.

"You sure you're going to be okay?" Aaron asked.

Jimmy nodded. "You go ahead and chop for a while," he said. "I'll be right in a minute."

Aaron lifted the axe out of the dirt, but kept his eyes focused on the man. Jimmy pressed the inhaler to his lips and pushed the button. His arms and shoulders both shook a little as the medicine forced its way into his lungs. Aaron hefted the axe in his hands a couple of times to get a feel for its weight. The blade was heavy, the handle worn smooth from years of use.

"You remind me a little bit of my son," Jimmy said when he could breathe again. "I suppose he was just a couple of years older than you are now when he left." Jimmy set the inhaler down on the deck and removed a pack of cigarettes from his pocket. "That boy couldn't wait to get out of here," he said. "He claimed the place was suffocating him." Jimmy struck a match on the side of the deck and lit his cigarette. "Who knows?" He said. "Maybe it was."

Aaron raised the axe up over his head. The blade hung in the air for a moment, the metal catching a glint of sunlight before it fell. The wood in front of him shuddered briefly, the falloff thudding onto the dampened earth below. Jimmy nodded his approval.

"I never used to let David chop wood," the man said. "I was always afraid he was going to hurt himself. I think he resented that—thought I didn't trust him."

Aaron lifted the falloff out of the dirt. "So how come you trust me, then?"

Jimmy shrugged and stared at the end of his cigarette. "You ain't my son," he said.

//

Aaron quickly fell into an easy rhythm: lift, chop, stack. In an hour he managed to work his way through half the pile. He was breathing hard, his face and arms damp with sweat. Taking a break, he leaned against the handle of the axe.

"You said your son moved away. Do you and your boy still talk?"

Jimmy tossed the butt of his cigarette out into the gravel. "David died a couple years back," he said. "Car accident up in Whitehorse."

"I'm sorry. I didn't know."

"Not your fault. Not anyone's fault, really. Sometimes things just happen." Jimmy stood and brushed wood chips from his legs.

"I suppose that'll do for a time," he said. "We'd best be getting back inside now."

Jimmy knelt and gathered a bundle of wood into his arms and Aaron did the same. The boy clutched three pieces of firewood to his chest and followed Jimmy up onto the porch. The front door jangled as it swung open in front of them. Jimmy knelt in front of the fireplace and deposited his load of wood onto the hearth. He opened the door to the stove and pushed several pieces into the flames. Aaron dropped to his knees and let his own burden tumble onto the floor beside him. Jimmy stacked these into a neat pile behind the stove.

"The lunch crowd'll be in soon," Jimmy said. "Truckers mostly. If you're lucky, maybe you can hitch a ride with one of them." The man closed the stove and pushed himself back to his feet. Aaron stood as well.

"Restroom's at the end of the counter if you need to wash up," Jimmy said.

//

As Aaron emerged from the washroom, Grace flashed him a warm smile.

"I thought you'd left us," she said.

Aaron slid onto a stool at the end of the bar. In the kitchen, Jimmy ducked into the cooler, the metal door thumping closed behind him. Grace set a place setting of silverware in front of the boy.

"That was a good thing you did," she said. "Helping out, I mean." Grace removed a jar of ketchup from her apron and placed this on the counter as well. The waitress straightened the silverware and pushed it closer to the boy. Her left hand toyed with the ketchup, her fingers twirling the jar around and around. "It wasn't so bad before David left," she said. "But ever since then it's been all we can do just to keep up."

For the third time that day, Grace touched a hand to Aaron's arm, her fingers lightly brushing the scratches on the back of his wrist. Behind her, Jimmy emerged from the cooler, and Grace quickly pulled her hand back. The woman lowered her eyes and began loading napkins and silverware onto a serving tray. Jimmy eyed the two for a moment, his expression wary. The man frowned and reached for his jacket.

"We're out of lettuce," he said. "I'm going to run across to the market and see if Jack's got any left in the bins."

After the man had gone, Grace carried her tray across the room and set it down on the table closest to the door. When she spoke, her voice was barely audible, so quiet that at first Aaron thought she was talking to herself.

"I remember my son telling me once how everything is always in motion," she said. "Atoms, planets. Everything moving—even the sun. I remember being surprised by that idea—that even when we're standing still we're moving."

Grace leaned out over the table and placed a napkin and silverware in front of the window. She straightened the napkin with her fingers and then reached back for another.

"When David first moved away it was hard," she said. "He and Jimmy had been at each other's throats for most of a year. The day he left, David wouldn't even speak to his father. Never even said goodbye." Grace lifted her tray and moved to the next table in line. She began laying out place settings there just as she had at the table before.

"When David called to say he was coming home for Christmas, I thought it might be a chance for the two of them to set things right. Jimmy wouldn't say so, but I could tell he missed the boy." Grace looked outside. A car passed by on the highway, its tires spitting mud and gravel into the air.

"There was a blizzard that night," Grace said. "The roads were nearly impassable. David should have stayed in Whitehorse. But he wanted to come home. He wanted to be with his family."

Across the road, Jimmy re-emerged from the market with a head of lettuce in each hand. The man paused at the roadway and watched as two trucks passed by in quick succession.

Grace turned and looked at Aaron. "You see, no matter how much we'd like the world to stay in one place, it just keeps moving. There's no way to stop it, really. We try to remain upright, to keep our balance, but the world just keeps spinning out from under us."

Her tray empty, Grace crossed the room and set the platter down on the counter. She slid onto the seat next to Aaron. "You don't have to go, you know. You could stay here with us. Lord knows Jimmy could use the help. We can't pay you much, but the room and the food would be free."

Aaron didn't know what to say to this. To buy himself time, he lifted his glass and took a sip of water. As he did so, Jimmy came back in through the front door. The man's stare slid from Grace to Aaron and back again.

"What have you been telling the boy, Grace?"

"Nothing. We were just talking, that's all."

Jimmy set the two heads of lettuce down on the counter and removed his coat. "The boy can't stay here, Grace, you know that.

You might think you can save them all, but you can't."

Grace stood quickly, both hands holding on to the counter. She glared at her husband for a moment, then pushed past him into the kitchen. Once she was gone, Jimmy turned to face the boy.

"I appreciate the help you gave me. I truly do. But we don't need your kind hanging around here." Jimmy reached under the counter and tore the lid off of an empty box. He handed this to the boy, then retrieved a marking pen from beside the cash register. He set this down next to the cardboard.

"What are these for?" Aaron asked.

"You can make a sign with them," Jimmy said. "Tell people where you want to go."

Aaron looked at the blank piece of cardboard. "And what if I don't know?"

Jimmy shrugged. "Then make something up," he said.

Aaron felt as if he had been slapped. He grabbed the marking pen and removed the cap. He thought for a moment, then began blocking out letters. He worked quickly, the felt tip tearing into the surface of the cardboard. When he was finished, Aaron spun the sign so that Jimmy could read it.

Jimmy nodded. "That seems about right," he said.

Aaron pushed himself away from the counter and stood. He felt flushed, hot. He needed air. His stomach rumbled, but he had no desire to eat. Aaron scooped the sign off the counter and turned to go. As he did, Grace stepped back into the room.

"Are you leaving?" She asked.

Aaron nodded. He didn't know what to say. The woman's eyes flickered from the boy's face to the sign in his hands.

"What's that you have?" she asked.

Aaron looked down at the scrap of cardboard. "It's nothing," he said. "Just a sign."

"What does it say?"

"It doesn't mean anything. I was just trying to be funny, that's all."

"Can I see it?"

Reluctantly, Aaron turned the sign so the woman could read it. Grace mouthed the words slowly, her lips forming each syllable in turn. When she was finished she grabbed the serving tray and began loading it with ketchup bottles. She didn't look at Aaron, but instead kept her head down, eyes hidden. Aaron looked again at the cardboard in his hands. The words written there stared back at him like an accusation: *Anywhere But Here,* they said.

"I think you ought to be going now," Grace told him.

Aaron nodded. He knew that he should say something—that he owed the woman some explanation. But he was young and tired and had already spent far too long in this lonely place.

Turning away from the couple, Aaron reached for the latch. The bell jangled briefly and Aaron silenced it with his hand. He stepped out through the opening and let the door slam hard behind him.

Creative Writing Scholarship
to the California State Summer School for the Arts

EmberJournal.org/scholarships/csssa

As part of our mission to support great new writers, the Empire & Great Jones Creative Arts Foundation is excited to sponsor a full annual scholarship for a high-school-aged writer to attend the CSSSA Creative Writing Program.

Established in 1987, CSSSA is a rigorous four-week pre-professional training program in multiple disciplines. Creative writing students receive individualized instruction in poetry, fiction, and scriptwriting. They work with an award-winning faculty in small groups and have opportunities to learn from visiting writers, literary agents, journalists, and poets.

Alumni of the Creative Writing program include bestselling author **Margaret Dilloway**; media voice and NPR contributor **Starlee Kine**, perhaps best known for her work on *This American Life*; award-winning playwright and director **Jon Tracy**; award-winning playwright and current chair of the CSSSA Creative Writing Department **Zay Amsbury**; and *Ember*'s own editor-in-chief, **Brian Lewis**.

The 2015 session will be held July 11 through August 7 at CalArts in Valencia, California. Each year's application deadline is February 28.

If you are a talented young author or poet of any genre, learn more or apply to the program at *csssa.org* knowing you have our full support!

Be a Sponsor. Be a Hero.

You can join us in supporting talented writers by donating to our scholarship fund at *EmberJournal.org/support*.

Your gift enables us to continue offering scholarships like this to deserving and talented writers, and you'll see the impact of your contribution as these students go on to become leaders and teachers in the writing community.

Submission Guidelines
emberjournal.org/submission-guidelines

AUDIENCE

Ember is a semiannual journal of poetry, fiction, and creative nonfiction for all age groups. Submissions for and by readers aged 10 to 18 are strongly encouraged.

HOW TO SUBMIT

Submissions are managed through our Submission Manager, powered by **Submittable**. If you submit by e-mail, we will direct you to use our Submission Manager instead. Postal submissions are not accepted. A link to the submission manager can be found at the bottom of our submission guidelines page at *emberjournal.org/submission-guidelines*.

FORMATS

Poetry
Most forms are considered, both metered and unmetered, traditional and experimental. Poems from 3 to 100 lines have the best chance of acceptance. You may submit up to three poems at a time, but a separate submission form must be completed for each poem.

Short Stories
Short Stories up to 12,000 words will be considered. However, more important than word count is the quality of your work: we are looking for excellent, polished writing that pulls us into an engaging story.

Flash Fiction
The ideal length for Flash Fiction submissions is about 500 to 750 words, but pieces up to 1500 words may be submitted in this category. Remember that Flash Fiction is not the same as "vignette;" even very short works should still present an interesting and compelling story.

Creative Non-Fiction
More than a journalistic presentation of fact, Creative Non-Fiction is the beautiful union of exposition and literature. Tell us a true story, and tell it well. Word count limits are the same as for Short Stories.

Rights & Rates

We purchase worldwide first publication rights in English. You retain all other rights (including other languages, audio, and reprint rights), but we ask that you not reprint the work in another publication for six months after it first appears in *Ember*. See our website for current minimum rates.

Content Tips & Suggestions

Avoid Profanity, Vulgarity, Sex, and Violence
As an all-ages publication, our refusal to print profanity/vulgarity is based on an understanding of our audience, not on censorship. Submissions with strong language will be rejected if they cannot be edited. Similarly, while allusions to the occurrence of love and sex, anger and violence may be integral to some stories, we tend to err on the side of making Ember accessible to middle-grade readers. Submissions with graphic and/or explicit descriptions of sex or violence will be rejected without comment.

Prose: Great Stories, Compelling Characters
Ember is looking for great writing that tells a compelling story, regardless of length. Even very short pieces, like flash fiction, should tell a story, though there will certainly be fewer dramatic elements developed than we'd see in a longer piece or novel. The presence of "story" is what distinguishes flash fiction from "vignette."

Poetry: Paint With Language
For poetry, we also look for a story, but the story may be implied. Of course, there is a lot more flexibility for poetry, and some styles tend to emphasize descriptive language over storytelling. We've also seen some poetry submissions which go too far, focusing so much on story that they are little more than prose stories with poem-style line breaks. So, for poetry, we tend to use the very subjective measure of accepting poems which make us say, "Wow!"

Be Accessible, Not Condescending
We believe that even our younger readers are smart and capable of advanced reasoning and interpretation. However, not every accepted piece will be appropriate for or of interest to ten-year-olds, who are the youngest readers in our target audience. Many readers will simply skip over stories and poems which exceed their developmental maturity. Submissions with the best chance of acceptance will be meaningful on some level to both older and younger readers without being condescending. We also consider works which require some maturity for full comprehension, so long as the content is not inappropriate for younger readers who might choose to explore the more advanced pieces.

About the Editor

Brian Lewis, founder and editor-in-chief, is an active member of the Editorial Freelancers Association, an alumnus of the California State Summer School for the Arts in Creative Writing, and a Senior Software Security Engineer. Raised in Northern California, he currently lives in Loomis with his wife and eight children.

About the Assistant Editor

Amberly Lewis is a high-school student who loves literature and started writing at a very young age. She has published a family newsletter and has completed a novella and several short stories. Besides writing fiction and poetry, Amberly plays violin and dances classical ballet. She is the oldest of eight children, and her sister **Æden Lewis** is a staff reader for *Ember.*

About the Staff

Ember: A Journal of Luminous Things is published by Empire & Great Jones Little Press and administered by the Empire & Great Jones Creative Arts Foundation, a non-profit 501(c)(3) organization. The high quality of this publication is made possible by a talented staff of skilled volunteers. Writer Liaison **Anne Bradshaw** not only manages the assigment of submissions to staff readers but compiles reader notes for the authors and poets who send us their work. **Angelic Sugai**, Layout Assistant, works with editor Brian Lewis to prepare new publications for print. **Katie Blanchette** is our Social Media Coordinator and helps fans and followers keep up with our news and events. **Two dozen volunteer readers**—adolescents, teens, and adults—read submissions and take notes on what they love ... and what they don't.

To learn more about joining our staff in any role, visit *emberjournal.org/jobs.*